To our friend

with many kind greetings,

Dagmar and Ole

Kiel, July 4, 1994

SYNOPSES OF THE ANTARCTIC BENTHOS
VOLUME 6
EDITORS: J. W. WÄGELE & J. SIEG

D. BARTHEL & O. S. TENDAL
ANTARCTIC HEXACTINELLIDA

THESES ZOOLOGICAE

VOLUME 23

EDITOR: RONALD FRICKE

Synopses of the Antarctic Benthos
Volume 6
Editors: J.W. Wägele & J. Sieg

Antarctic Hexactinellida
by
Dagmar BARTHEL & Ole S. TENDAL

CHAMPAIGN
KOELTZ SCIENTIFIC BOOKS
1994

ANTARCTIC HEXACTINELLIDA

Authors' adresses:

Dagmar Barthel
Abteilung Meeresbotanik
Institut für Meereskunde
Düsternbrooker Weg 20
24105 Kiel / Germany

Ole S. Tendal
Zoologisk Museum Københavns Universitet
Universitetsparken 15
2100 København Ø / Denmark

© Koeltz Scientific Books, D-6240 Königstein/Germany
ISBN 3-87429-359-9
Koeltz Scientific Books (USA), RR7, Box 39
Champaign, Illinois 61821, USA
ISBN 1-878762-54-0
ISSN 0934-8956

CONTENTS

FOREWORD

The Synopses of the Antarctic Benthos are designed to meet the need of zoologists and naturalists interested in the Antarctic ecosystem. All volumes are written by specialists in their own fields. It was intended to publish all the information needed for the identification leaving out data which are of interest only for specialized taxonomists. If you find specimens you cannot identify with the help of these volumes, your material may belong to a new species, which should be described carefully and as completely as possible. Please send this material to a specialist.

The series will not be complete because of two reasons: The Southern Ocean has until today many unexplored areas, in future many new species will be described which were not known to our authors; for some taxonomic groups no specialist could be found. Nevertheless we hope that the volumes will help all those working with the Antarctic benthos and that the efforts of the taxonomists who have given their knowledge, time and services to write a monograph will be used for the description and protection of one of the most untouched ecosystems of our planet.

J.W. Wägele, J. Sieg
(Editors)

1. INTRODUCTION

Hexactinellids are among the oldest known metazoans, their fossil record dating back to the Precambrian. The group flourished most in the Jurassic and Cretaceous, with pronounced differences in the respective faunal compositions. The comparison of fossil and recent hexactinellid faunas shows a decrease in the dominance of forms with very rigid, fused skeletons and predominance of forms with non-fused skeletons today. However, the actual transition from palaeozoic to mesozoic and recent hexactinellida is still not well understood. The origin and position of hexactinellids in relation to demosponges is a much discussed subject as well, the discussion being generally impaired by our scanty knowledge on hexactinellid biology. Thus, a great deal of work on recent hexactinellid biology is required in the future. This work includes the formulation of a fitting description of the group. At present, the only two features that with certainty can be said to be common to all hexactinellids, but lacking in demosponges and calcareans, is the possession of hexactine spicules and a largely syncytial soft tissue organization.

Today, about 450-500 living species of hexactinellids are recognized, the majority of them described on the basis of one-time finds. The greater number of species of this group is bathyal and abyssal. The Antarctic is one of the relatively few places where hexactinellids occur in shallow waters; with only 27 recognized species it contains a very restricted part of the known hexactinellid fauna. Our knowledge on the Antarctic hexactinellids is skewed, because in contrast to the shelf species, the majority of which are documented with a great number of samples, most of the Antarctic deep-sea species descriptions are based on single finds of fragments. It is in the deep-sea that we can expect a number of additional species to be found in the future.

Despite the species paucity, hexactinellids dominate many Antarctic benthic communities with respect to their biomass and abundance, sometimes accounting for more than 90% of the benthic biomass; a large number of organisms are associated with the living hexactinellids and hexactinellid spicule mats are important structural components in many Antarctic bottoms. Biological work on hexactinellids, however, was much hindered by difficulties with species identification. Until now, a key covering all Antarctic hexactinellids did not exist and certainly none of the existing keys is suitable for non-hexactinellid specialists.

In this volume, we have attempted to construct a key to be used by non-specialists working biologically or in related fields. In doing so, we had to make a number of adjustments: The book contains all presently known Antarctic species, but only them. All related non-Antarctic species, their diagnostic characters and the respective side-paths in the identification keys are omitted to avoid confusion as much as possible. Therefore, the use of this identification key is absolutely restricted to the Antarctic. In both key and single species description, we have chosen to present only those morphological characters which are of diagnostic value. This concerns specifically the spicule complements. As a rule, hexactinellids contain many different types of spicules, but only few of them are presently used in species identification. Thus, in working with the material, the researcher will encounter many more different spicule types than are mentioned in the key and the important ones will have to be discerned. A further difficulty in hexactinellid species identification is the sequence of character use, which does not proceed in the order of going from the more obvious gross morphology down to the smallest spicule category, but instead goes back and forth between characteristics at different levels. We therefore strongly advise, not to "jump" the sequence of the key, as this easily leads to misidentifications.

Acknowledgements

We thank the Deutsche Forschungsgemeinschaft who made the preparation of this volume possible with a fellowship granted to D. B. Jens Nielsen, who patiently prepared the spicule drawings and G. Brovad, who provided photographs of the preserved specimens, were indispensable in the preparation of this volume. We are grateful to Dr. Nicole Boury-Esnault for kindly putting at our disposal the manuscript of a sponge thesaurus she currently prepares with some other collegues, to be used in sorting out terminology.

2. HISTORY OF HEXACTINELLID WORK IN ANTARCTICA

The first hexactinellid from Antarctica was taken by the British naval expedition, led by Sir James Ross 1839-1843 onboard the famous exploring ships "Erebus" and "Terror". It came from the Ross Sea, and although represented only by scattered spicules, Carter (1872) erected for it the new genus *Rossella*. The species was named *R. antarctica*. This was a long shot, but *Rossella* later turned out to be the most important among the hexactinellid genera found in the region, both in terms of number of species and of abundance and biomass.

The next expedition to bring Antarctic hexactinellids to the knowledge of the world was the "Challenger" Expedition (1873-1876), during which a number of species were recorded and described from deep-sea localities in what is nowadays considered part of the subantarctic region (Prince Edward-, Crozet- and Kerguelen Islands).

When from about the turn of the century on the exploration of Antarctica was performed at a larger scale, a number of more or less comprehensive collections were sent back to Europe and worked up by specialists in different countries, viz. M. Burton and R. Kirkpatrick (Great Britain), E. Topsent (France), V.M. Koltun (Russia) and F.E. Schulze (Germany).

The first large collection of continental Antarctic hexactinellids was provided by the Expédition Antarctique Belge (1897-1899) onboard the "Belgica" from the Bellingshausen Sea. Nine species of hexactinellids were found, five of which were described as new to science, one of them representing a new genus, while two were already known from elsewhere, and two could be identified only to the genus because of fragmentation (Topsent 1902).

Quite a number of expeditions from different countries took benthos samples at accessible parts of the Antarctic shelf between 1900 and 1915 (France in the Gerlache Strait and off Graham Land; Germany off Wilhelm II Land; Great Britain in South Georgia, off Palmer Land, in the Scotia Sea, off Victoria Land and in parts of the Ross Sea; Sweden in South Georgia and off the Antarctic Peninsula). The results from these expeditions added both genera and species new for the Antarctic region, many of them also new to science.

Rather early the abundance of hexactinellids on the Antarctic mainland shelf was recognized, and it was shown to be particularly due to the occurrence of species of the family Rossellidae (Topsent 1911). Species of the genus *Rossella* itself occur only in the Antarctic region, with the exception of one Antarctic species found also in the southern part of South America and off South Africa, and one non-Antarctic species described from the North Atlantic (Topsent 1915).

Over time, many species and genera were described; however, a number of these resembled each other much, were based on scanty material and were often attributed very local distributions. A necessary revision was made by Burton (1929). He found the Antarctic hexactinellid fauna to comprise about 25 species, belonging to 18 genera and seven families. More than half of the species were shown to be endemic, a result that added to the then emerging picture of generally high endemism of the Antarctic fauna and pointed to an extended evolutionary history of the region.

Another important result was the demonstration of circumantarctic distributions of most shelf hexactinellid species, leaving little substance to the ideas of species being confined to more or less restricted faunal provinces.

The results of later expeditions have confirmed this picture. The number of accepted species has been further reduced (Koltun 1976), and more detailed circumantarctic distributions have been established (Koltun 1969, 1970).

This improved understanding of taxonomy and distribution of hexactinellids in Antarctica has made it possible now to enter other biological fields. Earlier authors pointed out locally high abundance of some species (Topsent 1902, 1912, 1913; Burton 1929) and this has been confirmed and extended in recent years (Belyaev & Ushakov 1957; Dell 1972; Koltun 1966, 1969, 1970; Ushakov 1964; Voss 1988; Barthel et al. 1990). Such widely spread mass occurrences invite investigations on species composition, population structure, growth processes, turnover, biochemistry and general ecology in order to understand the local ecosystem. By repeatedly conducted SCUBA diving observations in McMurdo Sound an important step towards the understanding of the ecological role of these animals was performed in shallow water (Dayton et al. 1970, 1974; Dayton 1978). More recently, ecological investigations on deeper living hexactinellids have been started. By employing a combination of bottom trawling and underwater photography, phenomena such as patchiness, species dominance, substrate utilization, population structure and relations to other fauna could be demonstrated and described in some detail (Barthel & Gutt 1992).

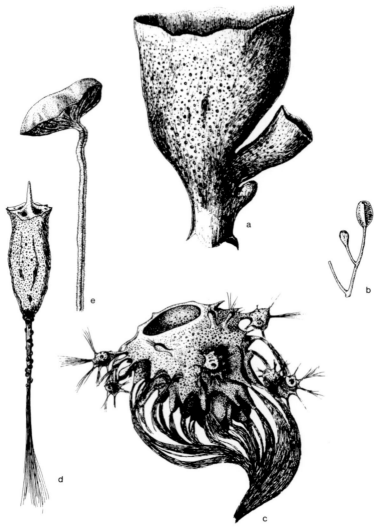

Fig. 1: Different morphological types of lyssacine hexactinellids. a) *Rhabdocalyptus mollis* F.E. Schulze, about 0.2 times natural size; b) *Sympagella nux* O. Schmidt, 0.6 times natural size; c) *Lophocalyx* (*Polylophus*) *philippinensis* Gray, about 0.6 times natural size; d) *Hyalonema thomsoni* W. Marshall, 0.4 times natural size; e) *Caulophacus elegans* F.E. Schulze, about 0.6 times natural size. After Schulze (1887, plates 22, 25, 34, 54 and 64).

3. MORPHOLOY AND ANATOMY

Gross Morphology

Hexactinellids are usually individuals with a radial symmetry and attain cup-, vase-, funnel-, tube- or mushroom-shapes (Fig. 1). The basic type of a hexactinellid can be seen as oval to eggshaped, attached to the substrate at the lower end. A central cavity ends with a large apical opening. Sometimes this unit of central cavity (termed gastral space in the older literature) and apical opening is referred to as osculum. The term osculum, however, should only be used for the very opening itself. The many smaller openings that cover the inner wall of the central cavity should be referred to as excurrent openings.

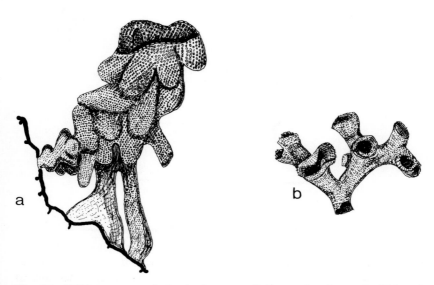

Fig. 2: Different morphological types of dictyonine hexactinellids. a) *Aphrocallistes bocagei* Wright, about 0.7 times natural size; changed; dark line: substrate; b) *Farrea occa* Bowerbank, about 1.2 times natural size. After Schulze (1887, plates 71, 83).

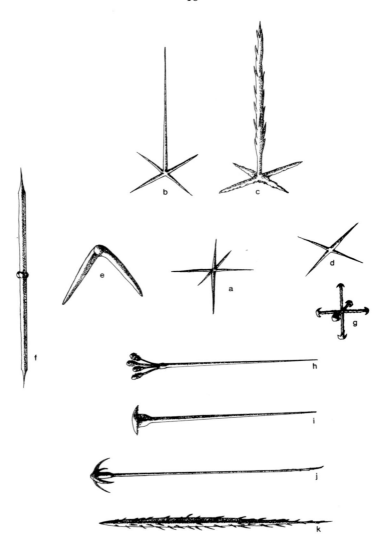

Fig. 3: Principal types of megascleres (actines) in Antarctic hexactinellids. a) hexactine (oxyhexactine); b) pentactine (oxypentactine; c) pentactine (pinule); d) tetractine (oxytetractine); e) diactine, boomerangshaped; f) diactine, straight; g) discohexactine; h) forkshaped spicule; i) clubshaped spicule; j) anchorshaped spicule; k) uncinate. Size ranges of each spicule type vary greatly between species.

Depending on the degree of folding of the flagellate chamber layer (see below), the hexactinellid walls can have very different thicknesses. In extreme cases (e.g. *Caulophacus* sp., Fig. 1e) the body walls can be bent outward and downward so much, that the cavity vanishes, and the inner sponge walls form the upper side of the sponge and the overall shape is that of a mushroom. The radial symmetry is masked in some groups, as the original tubes can have sidebulges (*Chonelasma, Aphrocallistes,* Fig. 2a) or form branches (*Eurete, Farrea,* Fig. 2b). In these cases, hexactinellids can resemble corals or bryozoans. While hexactinellids on hard bottoms are attached with solid base plates formed by excretion of amorphous silica, those living on soft bottom are anchored in the substrate with either long spicule root tufts or by stalks. Stalks mostly consist of many individual spicules cemented together (*Caulophacus, Hyalonema*); in the case of the famous *Monoraphis*, the stalk consists of a single giant spicule, from which the genus derives its name. Stalk fragments of up to 1.5 m length and 8.5 mm thickness are known.

With the exception of the true deep-sea species, hexactinellids found in the Antarctic are usually vase- or sackshaped with sturdy walls that easily reach several cm in thickness and several decimeters in heigth. The inner surface can be lined by a spicule reticulum, but there are also species lacking it. Externally, the surface can be even or covered by a more or less dense array of conules. Conules partly bear spicule tufts perpendicular to the surface. Even surfaces can be devoid of large protruding spicules, in other species the whole surface is covered by a dense spicule felt.

Skeletal elements and basic skeleton structure

The mineral skeleton of hexactinellids is siliceous and generally differentiated into spicules; some species, however, can form amorphous silicate masses to attach to hard substrates. The basic spicule type is the hexactine, which is only found in the Hexactinellida and from which the name of the class is coined. The hexactine consists of three siliceous rods which cross at right angles in one common center (Fig. 3a, g), giving rise to six rays. Each rod contains an organic axial filament which is square in cross-section (Reiswig 1971); originally, the spicule is secreted around this axial filament. All differently shaped spicule categories found in hexactinellids are considered derivatives of the hexactine. Hexactinellid spicules come in two size classes, which are distinct in position and function. The megascleres are several hundred μm to several tens of cm long; the

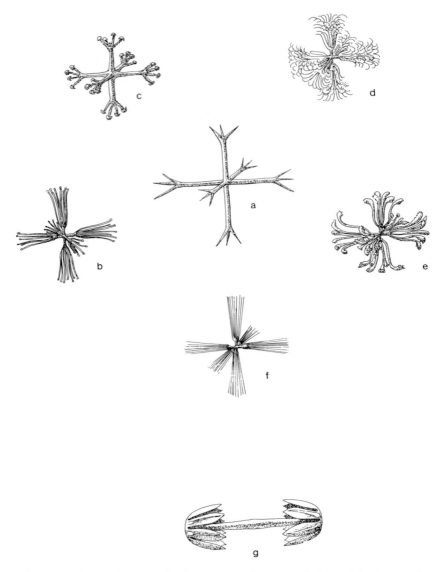

Fig. 4: Principal types of microscleres (hexaster derivates) in Antarctic hexactinellids. a) hexaster (oxyhexaster); b) calycocome; c) discohexaster; d) plumicome; e) floricome; f) graphiocome; g) amphidisc. Size ranges of each spicule type vary greatly between species.

19

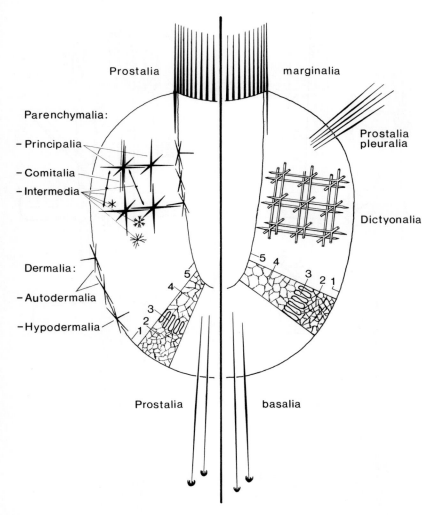

Fig. 5: Schematic drawing of spicule and soft tissue arrangement in hex-actinellid sponges. Spicule names given are those used in this volume. The names of the inner dermalia on the wall of the oscular cavity correspond to those of the outer dermalia. 1: outer dermal membrane; 2: outer trabecular layer; 3: flagellate chamber layer; 4: inner trabecular layer; 5: inner dermal membrane. Based on a drawing by Schulze (1887), changed.

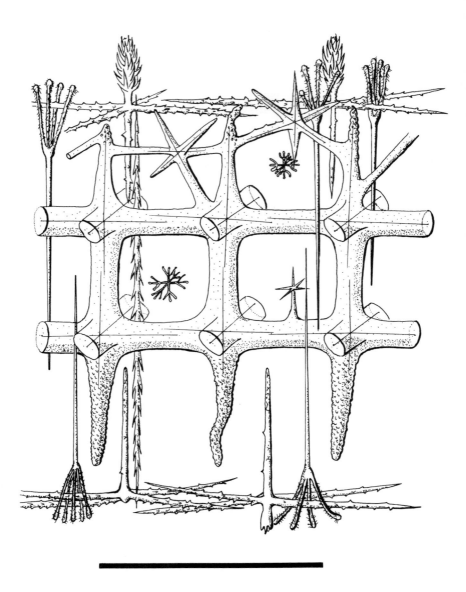

Fig. 6: Dictyonine skeleton of *Eurete erectum*, section through the entire wall, scale bar 500 μm. After Schulze (1899, plate 17).

microscleres are usually several tens to several hundred μm in their largest dimension.

The basic types of the megascleres are given the suffix actines. Besides by their size, they are characterized by the fact that the axial filament is present in all rays. In the pentactines (Fig. 3b, c), one ray is reduced, while the loss of a whole axis results in the four rayed tetractines (Fig. 3d). The loss of one more ray leads to the very rare form of triactines. Is only one of the original axes left, the spicule is called a diactine (Fig. 3e, f). It resembles very much the oxea of demosponges, but the different origin of the diactine is reflected by the presence of the rudimentary axial cross in the centre. Finally, there are also monactines, in which only one of the original rays is left. In contrast to diactines, the axial cross of monactines is at one end of the rod; it is often difficult to distinguish between these two types, and the true nature of some of the straight, rod shaped actines (e.g. Fig. 3h - k), like the uncinate, is still unclear (e.g. Schulze 1887, Kirkpatrick 1910b, Ijima 1927).

The basic type of the microsclere is the hexaster. The many hexaster derived spicules are not the result of reductions of rays or axes like in the megasclere development, but of formation of terminal ray appendages lacking axial filaments (Fig. 4a-f). In some cases the change in shape is so drastic that the hexaster nature of a given spicule is not immediately evident, like in the amphidiscs (Fig. 4g).

The positioning of the various spicule types within the hexactinellid body is highly differentiated (Fig. 5), much more so than in the other sponge classes. The main skeletal structure is formed by the megascleres, which can either be present as single free spicules (*Lyssacina*), or rigidly fused (*Dictyonina*, Fig. 6) (see chapter 7.1). Microscleres are dispersed between the major skeletal tracts, and can additionally be arranged in an extremely regular way in the dermal skeleton. While it is evident that the mineral skeleton serves to support the soft tissue, the precise connection between different soft parts and different skeletal elements is as yet not investigated. Especially the exact location and function of the microscleres found in most hexactinellids has as yet to be investigated.

Anatomy

Hexactinellids are primarily constructed syncytially, in contrast to Demospongiae and Calcarea which are composed of single cells embedded in a noncellular gel-like mesenchyme. The body wall consists of 5 layers: outer dermal membrane, outer trabecular layer, flagellate chamber layer, inner trabecular layer and inner dermal membrane (Fig. 7). The dermal membrane consists of extensions of the syncytium forming the underlying trabecular layer. Thus, it is very thin (1-2.5 μm) and lacks the mechanical resilience found in many demosponge dermal membranes. The incurrent openings are the free spaces between these dermal tissue strands and have a width of 4-30 μm (*Rhabdocalyptus dawsoni*, Mackie & Singla 1983). Underlying the dermal membrane is the trabecular layer, a very open, lacunar network formed by a syncytium suspended between the skeletal tracts and strengthened by a backbone-like collagenous mesolamella. So far, three different types of junctions have been found in hexactinellid soft tissues: a) Open cytoplasmic bridges, i.e. a thin plasma connection between adjacent cells; there is no difference in cytoplasm on both sides of the connecting bridge. This connection is typical for the trabecular layer. b) Plugged bridges, also called perforate septal partitions; in this case, the cytoplasmic connection is partly sealed by a disc-shaped plug with small cylindrical pores in it (for details see Mackie & Singla 1983). Usually, there are marked differences in the cytoplasm on both sides of the plugged bridge, suggesting that the plug is an effective barrier against movement of cell organelles. This type is found throughout the choanosyncytium, and occasionally in the trabecular layer. c) Septate junctions; in this case, parallelly lying cell membranes are connected to each other by fine septae. Septate junctions occur between the trabecular layer and free cells and connect trabeculum with collar bodies (see below).

Embedded in the syncytial matrix are a few free cell types; among those recognized with certainty are amoebocytes, archaeocytes and thesocytes (storage cells). The layer of thimble-shaped flagellate chambers is suspended between the two trabecular layers; in literature, the chambers are often named choanocyte chambers in correspondance to other sponge groups. However, they do not consist of choanocytes, but are a complicated structure (Mackie & Singla 1983) composed of basically two elements, namely an extension of the trabecular layer and a choanosyncytial layer (Fig. 8). On the incurrent side of the flagellate chamber layer, extensions of the trabecular syncytium condense into a layer comparable

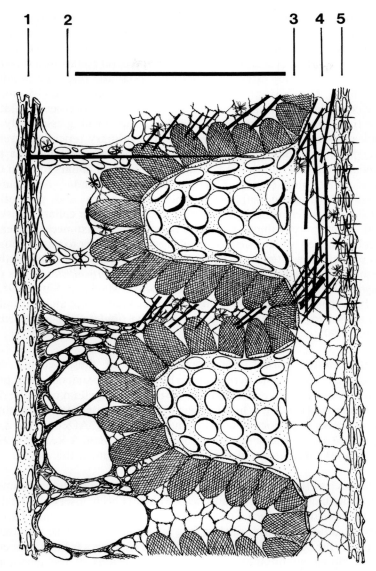

Fig. 7: Vertical wall section of the lyssacine *Bathydorus fimbriatus*. 1: outer dermal membrane; 2: outer trabecular layer; 3: flagellate chamber layer; 4: inner trabecular layer; 5: inner dermal membrane. Scale bar 1 mm. After Schulze (1887, plate 58), changed.

to the dermal membranes. This structure is called primary reticulum. Embedded in the primary reticulum are archaeocyte-derived choano-blasts. These are thought to stretch out processes to the inner, i.e. excurrent surface; the processes in turn develop microvilli collars and flagella. This unit of cell body extension, microvilli collar and flagellum is called collar body. The choanoblast produces lateral stolons which give rise to more collar bodies. At a later stage, the collar bodies become separated from their choanoblast by plugged bridges, thus forming essentially an enucleate structure. Cell processes from the primary reticulum stretch through perforations in the choanosyncytium into the lumen of the flagellated chamber and merge around the microvilli collars to form the secondary reticulum (Fig. 9). The function of this secondary reticulum is probably hydrostatic, supporting the collar edges and preventing backflow of water by occluding the spaces between the collars (Reiswig 1979). Primary reticulum and choanosyncytium are connected to each other by plugged bridges. Gaps in both layers allow water to pass through, then particles are filtered out by the microvilli collars. This construction scheme has so far been observed in the species *Aphrocallistes vastus* (by Reiswig 1979) and *Rhabdocalyptus dawsoni* (by Mackie & Singla 1983). The basic construction with primary and secondary reticulum has also been shown for the Antarctic species *Rossella fibulata*[1] (by Salomon & Barthel 1990).

In *Aphrocallistes vastus*, the exact structure of the flagellum was investigated. The flagella were found to have two wing-shaped lateral projections (vanes) which reach from the basis of the flagellum up to the rim of the microvilli collar (Mehl & Reiswig 1991). The presence of these vanes had previously been documented in demosponges (e.g. Afzelius 1961 a, b, Feige 1966) and Calcarea (e.g. Simpson 1984), and Mehl & Reiswig (1991) anew discuss the question of poriferan monophyly under this aspect.

While much of the internal structure observed so far seems to be common to all hexactinellids, some variations have already been observed. The dictyonine hexactinellid *Farrea occa* has an internal structure much like *A. vastus*, *R. dawsoni*, and *A. vanhoeffeni*, but additionally to the secondary reticulum, the central region of the flagellate chambers is lined by a perforated "inner membrane", consisting of extensions of the secondary reticulum into the chamber (Reiswig & Mehl 1991). The authors propose

---

[1] Salomon & Barthel provisionally identified the species as *Aulorossella vanhoeffeni*, but it later turned out to be *Rossella fibulata*, previously known from one fragment only.

25

that the membrane might serve to effect cessation of flagellar activity and thus water flow in individual chambers; furthermore, the inner membrane could also assist in collection and outward transport of undigestible material, as detritus aggregations in portions of this inner membrane could be documented.

In *Dactylocalyx pumiceus,* the secondary reticulum is missing, but functionally replaced by "fibrous network" at the same site. Furthermore, the perforated plugs between syncytial and cellular elements observed in the other three species, could not be documented for *D. pumiceus* as yet (Reiswig 1991a). These few investigations raise questions about species relations within the Hexactinellida, but more studies would be needed to resolve these problems.

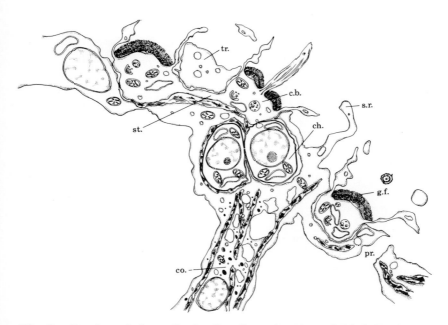

Fig. 8: Portion of the wall of a flagellate chamber of *Rhabdocalyptus dawsoni*. Abbreviations: c.b. collar body; ch. choanoblast; co. cord region; g.f. glycoprotein filament array; pr. prosopyle; st. stolon; s.r. secondary reticulum; tr. trabecular tissue. From Mackie & Singla (1983).

Usually, each hexactinellid flagellate chamber opens directly into an excurrent canal; the spaces between the chambers can be, but are not necessarily sealed by a thin membrane. In other cases, flagellate chambers merge with each other, and the filtering system turns out to be a continuous folded layer of primary and secondary reticulum and choanosyncytium. In species with thick walls, like in the Antarctic rossellids, folding can be very extensive. The excurrent side of the hexactinellid body is again provided by a trabecular syncytium, but the lacunar spaces are larger than on the incurrent side. The inner dermal layer is structurally like the outer dermal layer, but the spicule complements of the incurrent and excurrent layers are often different. Hexactinellids lack spongine and have only very little amorphous mesohyl substance stretching backbone-like through the syncytial tissue strands; thus, their tissues are much more loose than those of demosponges. The necessary rigidity is provided almost exclusively by the siliceous skeleton.

27

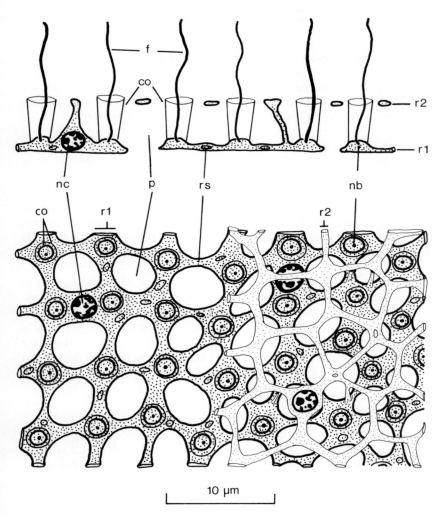

Fig. 9: Wall of the flagellate chamber of *Aphrocallistes vastus* seen from the side (above) and from inside (below). The basic tissue layer is composed of the primary reticulum giving rise to the secondary reticulum and of collar bodies giving rise to flagella and microvilli collars. Abbreviations: co collar; f flagellum; nb collar body; nc nucleus; r1 primary reticulum plus collar bodies; r2 secondary reticulum; rs connecting strands of primary reticulum; p prosopyle. After Reiswig (1979), changed.

4. TERMINOLOGY

Terminology in hexactinellids, especially that pertaining to the skeletal elements, is suffering greatly from the fact that over time a number of researchers have erected their own systems. Presently used systems are the result of repeated modification, usually consisting of splitting up previous categories of spicules into a number of subcategories.

Treatises on terminology include the original work by Schulze (1887), the nicely illustrated lists of spicules for all sponges by Schulze & v. Lendenfeld (1889) and by Delage & Hérouard (1899), Kirkpatrick's (1910a,b) attempt to clean up the spicule naming in hexactinellids and Ijima's (1927) work, which includes a great deal of discussion on origin and relations of spicule types to each other. For a thorough description and terminology of hexactinellid soft parts, the works of Mackie & Singla (1983) and Reiswig & Mehl (1991) should be consulted.

For reasons of clarity and simplicity, we use as few and simple terms as possible and leave out all names of spicules not existing in Antarctic hexactinellids, but we have included the terms more often encountered in special literature, to facilitate use of original descriptions. Despite what is found in some textbooks, it is incorrect to use terms devised for demosponges to describe structures in hexactinellids, because more often than not there is no basic homology.

General terms

Hexactinellida: The term was coined by Schmidt (1870) for all sponges with siliceous triaxone spicules. The basic spicule type is the hexactine, which consists of three siliceous rods which cross at right angles in one common center, giving rise to six rays.

Hyalospongiae: Synonym for hexactinellida; term coined by Vosmaer (1886).

Triaxonida, Triaxonia: Synonym for hexactinellida; term coined by Schulze (1887); the name triaxonida refers to the fact that the spicules of this sponge group are constructed of rays arranged along three axes which are perpendicular to each other.

Gross morphology

Choanosyncytium: Tissue in the walls of the flagellate chambers. For detailed description see Chapter 3, Morphology and Anatomy and Fig.8.

Conule: Coneshaped to rounded protrusion on the outer, incurrent side of hexactinellids. Conules can vary in size from somewhat less than one to several cm height and can be with or without protruding spicule bundles. Conules do not bear oscula. They are often found in rossellids (Fig. 1c). Note: Because of gross morphological variability in some species, presence or absence of conules can be of doubtful value as identification character.

Dermal membrane: Membrane limiting the tissue against the surrounding sea water both on the outer (inhalant, incurrent) and inner (exhalant, excurrent, oscular) side of the body. The membranes are extensions of the subdermal syncytial trabecular layers on both sides of the flagellate chamber layer (Figs. 5, 7). The outer membrane is perforated by numerous incurrent openings, the dermal pores, the inner dermal membrane is perforated by excurrent pores, which are not referred to as dermal pores; no special term exists for the excurrent pores. In some original descriptions, the inner dermal membrane is referred to as the gastral membrane, a term which should be avoided, as the oscular cavity is not a true gastral space. In descriptions where the term gastral membrane is used for the inner side of the body wall, the term dermal membrane refers to the outer side only.

Dermal pores: Incurrent openings on the outer (or in the mushroom shaped Caulophacidae the under) side of hexactinellid body wall through which water enters the sponge. Note: The term ostia used for the incurrent openings in demosponges and calcareans should be avoided in hexactinellids, because the structures are not homologous.

According to Mackie and Singla (1983), the size of the dermal pores would be in the range of 4-30 μm diameter (*Rhabdocalyptus dawsoni*).

Dictyonine skeleton: Skeleton in which the large individual main spicules - mostly hexactines - have become fused and form a continuous netlike main skeleton (Figs. 5, 6), in which the single contributing spicules cannot be delimited from each other any more. Dictyonine skeletons can be single- or multilayered; in the latter case several sheets of network lie parallel to each other. The network can be regular or more irregular. Both number of layers and degree of regularity of network are identification characters. Within the spaces of the dictyonine skeleton there are usually loose spicules of different categories.

Excurrent side: Side of the body, on which the water leaves the sponge through the efferent openings. In tubular, sack- or vaseshaped species the inside, i.e. the lining of the oscular cavity, is the excurrent side. In some mushroom-shaped species (e.g. *Caulophacus*, Fig. 1e) it is the upper side.

Exhalant side: See Excurrent side.

Flagellate chamber layer: Layer of round to thimble-shaped flagellated chambers. The chambers can either merge with each other at the excurrent side, thus representing in reality a continuous, folded layer of choanosyncytium, or they can be connected to each other by membranaceous extensions of the trabecular layer, called membrana reuniens by Schulze (1887). In thickwalled specimens, the flagellate chamber layer is arranged in secondary and tertiary foldings.

Inner dermal membrane: See Dermal membrane.

Inner trabecular layer: See Trabecular layer.

Incurrent side: Side of the body wall, where the water enters the sponge body through the dermal pores. In tubular, sack- or vase-shape species this is the outer side, in some mushroom-shaped species the underside. In some Dictyonina, the whole visible surface is the incurrent side, the oscula are borne on the tips of the branches.

Inhalant side: See Incurrent side.

Lyssacine skeleton: A condition where the large hexactines or derivates thereof forming the main skeleton are not fused with each other (Figs. 5, 7). In some cases the megascleres can partly be cemented together, but never form the compound structure of a dictyonine skeleton. Besides the megascleres of the main skeleton there are a number of additional spicules of different categories found in different parts of the body. Schulze (1887) distinguishes between the principal supporting hexactines, which he calls principalia, and comitalia, i.e. the diactines aligned with these main skeleton hexactines. Spicules that have no precisely defined position in relation to the main skeleton and that are loosely attached to the trabecular strands are referred to as intermedia by him (See also Fig. 5).

Main skeleton: Part of the skeleton that is the main structural support in the body wall. In the Dictyonina this will be the fused dictyonine skeleton, in the Lyssacina the large hexactines and derivates thereof forming the bulk of the wall skeleton. The main skeleton is complemented by various categories of microscleres and the dermal and hypodermal spicules. Schulze's (1887) collective term for all spicules supporting trabecular syncytium and choanosyncytium is parenchymalia.

Multilayered skeleton: See Dictyonine skeleton.

Oscular cavity: The hollow space in hexactinellids, into which the efferent canals unite. The outer opening of the oscular cavity is the osculum (see there).

Osculum: General term for excurrent openings in sponges. The use of this and related terms like oscular cavity, preoscular cavity, suboscular cavity etc. is unfortunately quite inconsistent; especially the word osculum has repeatedly been used for the oscular cavity as well. In this volume we use the term osculum strictly for the opening only. When other literature is used, the use of the term will have to be checked each time. In some species, f.ex. *Euplectella aspergillum*, the osculum is covered by a sieve plate closing the oscular cavity. The large osculum of the Antarctic rossellids is open, but the inner body wall lined by thimble-shaped efferent openings is in some species covered by a fine lacelike network. It is at present not clear, how sieveplates and the lacelike meshwork morphologically relate to each other, but to avoid further confusion, the individual efferent openings should not be referred to as oscular cavities.

Outer dermal membrane: See Dermal membrane.

Outer trabecular layer: See Trabecular layer.

Secondary reticulum: Part of the flagellated chambers in hexactinellids, not found in any other sponge group. The part of the trabecular syncytium forming the outer lining of the flagellate chambers grows extensions into the chamber cavity around the microvilli collars, thus forming an upper supporting network (Figs. 8, 9).

Sieve plate: Coarse-meshed netlike structure composed of spicules and organic constituents, covering the oscular opening in some hexactinellid groups. A well known example is *Euplectella aspergillum*.

Single-layered skeleton: See Dictyonine skeleton.

Spiculum: Every independent and originally isolated skeletal element secreted by the hexactinellids themselves.

Trabecular layer: Wide-meshed syncytial layers inbetween dermal membranes and flagellate chamber layer. Usually, the meshsize of the trabecular layer below the outer, i.e. incurrent dermal membrane is smaller than that of the trabecular layer between the openings of the flagellated chambers and the inner, i.e. excurrent dermal membrane. The surficial extensions of the trabecular syncytium form the dermal membranes (Fig. 7). According to drawings by Schulze (1887, 1904), the dermal pores are in the range of several tens to about 100 μm, Mackie & Singla (1983) measured 4-30 μm in living *Rhabdocalyptus dawsoni*.

Spicules

Actine: A ray or point; used as a suffix when referring to the number of rays or points of a sponge spicule.

Amphidisc: Microsclere, at each end of which a convex expansion occurs, which bears six or more backwardly bent marginal teeth (Fig. 4g). Because of the structure of the axial filament, amphidiscs are considered a phylogenetic derivate of hexaster (compare Kirkpatrick 1910). Note: Amphidiscs and other hexasters mutually exclude each other in hexactinellid skeletons. Thus, where the term hexaster is used in the literature, it is usually meant for non-amphidiscs only. We follow this custom. In single species, amphidiscs can occur in up to three different size classes, termed micramphidisc, mesamphidisc and macramphidisc in some original descriptions.

Anchorshaped spicule: See Monactine and Fig. 3j.

Axial filament: Organic filament in the center of each spicule. In spicule formation the axial filament is laid down first and the siliceous material is secreted around it. In hexactinellids, the extension of the axial filament is the character used to distinguish between the two principle classes of spicules, the hexactines or megascleres and hexasters or microscleres. Regardless of size, a spicule is called a hexactine, when the axial filament extends into all rays and branches. Actines with less than 6 rays can be traced back to the ancestral hexactine because in many cases the axial filament still bears tiny rudimentary knobs in the places where the reduced rays would have originated. If the distal branches of a spicule do not contain axial filaments, these branches are considered outgrowths (terminal rays, appendages) of the ancestral spicule; these forms are called hexasters or their derivates. Regardless of their actual size, they belong to the microsclere category.

Basalia: See Prostralia and Fig. 5.

Canalaria: See Dermal spicules.

Calycocome: Variant of hexaster, with short principal rays that have several long, outward curved appendages. The appendages are slightly S-curved, so each principal ray bears a chalice-like structure on its tip (Fig. 4b)

Clubshaped spicule: See monactine and Fig. 3i.

Dermal spicules: Spicules located in the dermal membrane, sometimes with one or more rays protruding outward; most often large hexactines or pentactines (Fig. 5). Called dermalia (for the outer dermal layer) and gastralia (for the inner dermal layer) by Schulze (1887), who divides them into several groups: autodermalia (autogastralia) which lie either completely or at least with their axial cross in the outer (inner) dermal membrane, canalaria, whose axial cross lies in the membrane which lines the efferent canals, and hypodermalia, which are just beneath the dermal membrane and have one ray pointing inwards. The hypodermalia are a somewhat paradox group, as their axial cross can in some species be situated on the surface or above the dermal membrane. This is especially developed in the genus *Rossella*, where large hypodermalia can protrude several cm above the sponge surface and the tangential rays of pentactines can form veil-like covers. Schulze (1887) includes these special hypodermalia in his group prostralia (see there).

Diactine: Reduced hexactine with only two rays left (Fig. 3e, f). Diactines can be either straight or bent, the latter variant often being boomerang-shaped.

Discohexactine: Hexactine with a transverse disc at the end of each principal ray (Fig. 3g).

Discohexaster: Hexaster with a transverse disc on the outer end of each terminal ray (Fig. 4c).

Floricome: Hexaster with S-shaped terminal rays, which are arranged in a whorl like the petals of a lily, and which enlarge at their outer end into a thickened terminal plate, arched outwards, and provided with external marginal teeth or claws (Fig. 4e).

Forkshaped spicule: See monactine and Fig. 3h.

Graphiocome, Graphiohexaster: Hexaster, where the ends of the principal rays bear a bundle of long fine terminal rays in a brush-like manner (Fig. 4f). The terminal rays of each principal ray are mostly parallel to each other, but can also spread out in all directions. This variant is called pappocome in some original descriptions. We use the general term graphiocome, as the degree of spreading of the rays is not always easy to see.

Hexactine: 6-rayed megasclere in which the three axes are at a 90° angle to each other (Fig. 3a).

Hexaster: 6-rayed microsclere in which the three principal axes are at a 90° angle to each other, and in which the rays are all equal (Fig. 4a). In contrast to hexactines, the principal rays bear terminal rays or appendages without axial filament. These appendages can attain very different shapes, like chalices and can bear discs or knobs at their ends, which give rise to the names of the various hexaster derivates. Derivates found in Antarctic hexactinellids are calycocomes (Fig. 4b), floricomes (Fig. 4e), graphiocomes (Fig. 4f), plumicomes (Fig. 4d) and discohexasters (Fig. 4c). The more rounded variants of hexasters are often referred to as rosettes in original descriptions. Note: Even though phylogenetically amphidiscs are hexaster derivates as well, the term hexaster is only used for non-amphidiscs in this context.

Hypodermal spicules: Spicules belonging to and situated immediately below the dermal layer, often with rays extending into the trabecular syncytial network (Fig. 5). In special cases, hypodermal spicules can protrude above the sponge surface (see prostralia). In hexactinellid identification, care has to be taken to keep hypodermal spicules and main skeleton spicules apart. In practice, this often requires separate spicule preparations (see chapter Sampling and Preservation). See also dermal spicules.

Macrosclere: See megasclere.

Marginalia: See prostralia.

Megasclere: Hexactines and derivates thereof; they are characterized by the presence of an axial filament in all the rays. Note: In some species hexactines can be very small, but are still called megascleres, to clarify their origin. Some workers (e.g. Koltun 1966) prefer the term macrosclere to megasclere.

Microsclere: In hexactinellids general term for hexasters and their different derivates and amphidiscs (Fig. 4). They are characterized by the fact that an axial filament is found in the principal rays only, but not in the secondary rays or appendages. The term microsclere describes the fact that these spicules are usually rather small. However, there are a number of hexaster-derived forms which can be large if compared to other spicules in the same skeleton. Nevertheless they would be counted among the microscleres to clarify their origin.

Monactine: Hexactine derivate; only one of the original 6 rays is left, the cross of the axial filament with 5 rudimentary rays is situated at the usually rounded head of the rod. The head can be enlarged, so as to give the spicule a clubshaped appearance (clavule of Ijima 1927) (Fig. 3i); a special variant of the clubshaped type is the anchor-shaped spicule, which has two or several backwards bent hooks at one end (Fig. 3j). In some species, the hooks are twisted into a spiral whorl. Schulze (1887) calls this type ancora. Another type of monactine is the forkshaped spicule, which bears a number of distally extending rays (scopule of Ijima 1927) (Fig. 3h). In the latter case, the monactine identity of the spicule can be nearly masked. Note: The forkshaped spicule with 4 outgrowths is not a pentactine, as the "rays" are not at right angles to each other or to the principal ray. For the same reason, this spicule type is not a hexaster derivate. A discussion of this problem is given by Ijima (1927).

Oxy-: Prefix indicating rays tapering out to a sharp point.

Oxyhexactine: Hexactine with rays tapering out into a point (Fig. 3a).

Oxyhexaster: Hexaster with straight or bent terminal rays tapering out into a sharp point (Fig. 4a).

Pentactine: Hexactine derivate with one reduced ray (Fig. 3b).

Pinule: Pentactine or hexactine with one ray covered with spines directed outwardly, i.e. away from the axial cross (Fig. 3c).

Pleuralia: See prostralia.

Plumicome: Hexaster with numerous S-shaped terminal rays (Fig. 4d). The terminal rays are arranged in several close layers, so the whole structure has a feathery appearance.

Prostralia: Megascleres originating in the trabecular layer and extending far above the sponge surface (Fig. 5). This term comprises hypodermal hexactines and pentactines as well as diactines, the precise origin of which is as yet unclear. In some cases (e.g. *Rossella antarctica*), the tangential rays of hexactine or pentactine prostralia form a veil-like cover one to several cm above the surface. Depending on their position on the sponge body, Schulze (1887), who coined the terms, distinguishes between basalia, pleuralia and marginalia. Basalia: Prostalia which project downwards from the lower end of the body, and which form the basal root-tuft by which the sponge is fixed in the mud. Pleuralia: Prostalia which project beyond the outer surface of the lateral part of the body. Marginalia: Prostalia which project in wreath-like arrangement round the oscular margin. The hexactine and pentactine prostralia represent a paradox insofar, as their hypodermal origin is not immediately evident. In his 1887 redescription of the genus *Rossella* with the species *Rossella antarctica* erected by Carter (1873) on the basis of a few spicules, Schulze names special spicules protruding from surface conules simply as prostralia, without giving indication as to their probable origin, and uses the term hypodermalia only for smaller, truly hypodermally arranged spicules. In 1895 Schulze for the first time indicates the hypodermal nature of the Prostralia: "The pentactine hypodermalia have a tendency to move up above the dermal surface, so that they form a veil-like cover around the sponge body" (translation from German by D.B.). In describing the material from the Deutsche Tiefsee-Expedition Schulze (1904) consequently uses the term "Pentactinhypodermalia" and in 1911 lists the prostralia finally as a form of hypodermal spicules. We follow his classification despite its obvious awkwardness, as the true origin and construction site of this spicule class is still not clarified and we do not want to add to systems unnecessarily. In descriptions however, we will just use the term prostralia.

Rhabd: General term for a straight, rod-shaped spicule. Example: uncinate, Fig. 3k).

Spines: Minute thorns on spicules; absence, presence and pattern of spines are of great diagnostic importance in hexactinellid identification.

Spinulation: A condition of spicules in which they are wholly or partly covered with minute spines or thorns.

Stauractine: Other term for tetractine.

Swordshaped hexactines: Hexactines, in which one ray is much shorter than the rest; the spicule resembles a sword with one short ray as the hilt, the opposite prolonged ray as the blade and the four rays perpendicular to this axis as the hand protection.

Tauactine: Other term for triactine.

Tetractine: Hexactine derivate in which only 4 rays are left (Fig. 3d); usually, all rays lie in one plane, i.e. two axes are completely maintained. In rarer cases, one ray each of two axes is missing. In a number of original descriptions, the term stauractine is used instead of tetractine.

Triactine: Hexactine derivate in which only 3 rays are left. These three rays are usually not in one plane. The term tauactine is occasionally found instead of triactine.

Uncinate: Straight, rodshaped spicule pointed at both ends and covered all over with spines pointing into the same direction (Fig. 3k). The question whether uncinates are monactines, diactines or maybe even a special kind of microsclere is as yet unresolved. For discussions of the problem see Schulze (1887), Kirkpatrick (1910b) and Ijima (1927).

5. BIOLOGY

Our knowledge on the biology of hexactinellids is very scanty, as good material, especially live specimens, are not easily accessible.

The main distribution is in deeper waters (> 300 m), with about two thirds of all species living deeper than 1000 m, and half of these even deeper than 2000 m. The reasons for this distribution are still not well understood, but a preference for colder water, low particle concentration and generally stable conditions is mostly thought of importance.

The entire group Amphidiscophora pertains to the deep sea. Among the Hexasterophora, the Dictyonina can tolerate higher temperatures and are found in medium depths in tropical waters and in shallow coastal waters off British Columbia (Reiswig 1979); the Lyssacina need temperate to cold waters and belong mainly to the deep sea. An exception are the likewise cold waters of the Antarctic shelf, where members of the lyssacine family Rossellidae can be found as shallow as 30 m depth (Dayton et al. 1970).

Position on the bottom is primarily vertical/upright, but e.g. for *Euplectella aspergillum* Bidder (1930) reasoned that the sponge bends to align with the current to maximize flow of water through its body. Recent deep-sea photographs show this idea to be correct. When living on soft substrates, hexactinellids are anchored with a more or less long spicule root tuft (e.g. *Euplectella*), or with solid stalks (e.g. *Semperella*), which can in turn be anchored on the stalk of a dead specimen (e.g. *Caulophacus arcticus*). When growing on hard substrate, hexactinellids construct basal plates by secreting amorphous silicate in addition to spicules (Tuzet 1973). Some Antarctic rossellid sponges can adapt very well to the substrate available to them: In soft substrate or spicule mats they are anchored with spicule root tufts, while on gravel bottoms they attach to single stones and form stiltlike structures (Plate III); additionally, they can attach to large boulders, probably with the kind of solid base described above.

The mechanism of water flow through hexactinellids is somewhat different from that in demosponges. Choanocytes are absent in Hexactinellida; the flagellated chambers do not always form a completely closed layer, so hexactinellid tissue can be a rather open network. Thus, hexactinellids cannot produce low pressure conditions on the exhalant side, to suck water through the canal system, to the same extent as demosponges are able to do. However, in contrast to older concepts (Bidder 1923, 1930) which proposed the ambient water current to be totally responsible for perfusion in hexactinellids, water flow through these sponges is indeed mediated largely by flagellar action, which is unidirectional and can stop subsequent to irritation (Mackie 1979, Lawn et al. 1981, Mackie et al. 1983). Mechanical prodding or electrical stimulation of *Rhabdocalyptus dawsoni* from shallow (10-30 m) British Columbian coastal waters resulted in arrest of water flow, very likely due to flagellar arrest. Diverse experiments showed that the arrest is coordinated by a conducting system with a precise threshold of excitability. Conduction was unpolarized and the signal was transported with a mean velocity of 0.22 cms^{-1}. While it could be shown that signal transfer was not mediated chemically, its exact nature could not be established. Nerve cells do not exist in sponges, but that does not preclude the ability of hexactinellid syncytia to conduct electrical signals via waves of membrane depolarization. In nature, *R. dawsoni* was observed to arrest water flow when particle load in the water was unusually high, so the mechanism can serve to prevent the canal system to be clogged.

Recently, Reiswig (1991b) performed the first experiments on hexactinellid feeding with two shallow water species, *Rhabdocalyptus dawsoni* and *Aphrocallistes vastus*. He measured differences in total organic carbon (TOC), particulate organic carbon (POC) and dissolved organic carbon (DOC) between ambient and exhalant water. The data show a mean uptake of 56 ± 250 µg TOC l^{-1}, mostly as DOC in *R. dawsoni* and 77 ± 256 µg TOC l^{-1}, mostly as POC, in *A. vastus*. Because of the very high variability, Reiswig's own interpretation is hesitant. He states that the retention of mostly dissolved organic carbon by *R. dawsoni* is due to the "veil-supported biotic jungle", i.e. the epifauna community in the spicule veil. In contrast, the "naked" species *A. vastus* retains particles, including bacteria, as its primary food source. However, more research is needed in this field.

Knowledge about hexactinellid reproduction is not very extensive either. The most comprehensive study was performed by Okada (1928) on *Farrea sollasi* (Euretidae, Dictyonina). He found spermatozoa, eggs and parenchymella-like larvae incubated until a late stage within the parent sponge. The spicule complement in the larva is well developped, but no flagellae were found, therefore it is possible that the larvae cannot swim but drop to the substrate by the side of the parent sponge, dependent on currents for wider distribution. The only other documentation of sexual reproduction stages are finds of spermatogenesis stages in *Euplectella aspergillum* (Schulze 1880) and in *E. marshalli, Acanthascus cactus* and *Farrea occa* (Ijima 1901, 1903).

Asexual reproduction by budding has so far been documented only in members of the lyssacine families *Caulophacidae* and *Rossellidae*, it seems to be completely absent in the deep-sea confined group of amphidiscophorans. In the Antarctic, budding is regularly observed in one variety of *Rossella racovitzae*, forming clumps with buds and small sponges on softbottom, and far less frequent in other rossellid sponges. In some cases it is not clear, whether budding has taken place or whether the structure observed is the result of regeneration after injury of a single large specimen. Tissue material of the hexactinellid *Rhabdocalyptus dawsoni* was shown to possess a certain capability for *in vitro* reorganization after mechanical dissolution. After about 24 hours, cultured syncytial and cellular tissue components formed larger units, consisting of reaggregations of syncytial elements enclosing cellular elements like archaeocytes. The enclosing syncytium shows vigorous phagocytic activity and compartmentalization by means of plugged junctions. Finally, the aggregates degenerate, probably, because the structuring spicule framework is lacking (Pavans de Ceccatty 1982).

Growth rate and age of hexactinellids are generally unknown, because we lack means for their direct determination. Growth is probably extremely slow in most Antarctic species: While Dayton (1979) observed growth and reproduction (budding) in *Rossella racovitzae* within 2-3 years, *Scolymastra joubini* and *R. nuda* did not grow or recruit during a ten year observation period. Thus, we can assume the age of large Antarctic hexactinellids to be in the range of decades or several decennia.

In Antarctic benthic assemblages, hexactinellids play a special role (Barthel 1992a). They can dominate as to biomass and it is primarily their skeletons that form the spicule mats typical for many benthic communities, allowing the subsequent settlement of a number of other sponge species (Barthel 1992b, Barthel & Gutt 1992). In life, they are habitat to a large number of other organisms, which are partly specialized on living in sponges like the isopod *Gnathia calva* that lives in *Rossella racovitzae* (Wägele 1988), but more often are inquilines. Especially conspicuous are crinoids and holothurians that can often be seen to perch on the oscular rim of the large hexactinellids (e.g. Barthel et al. 1991, Dearborn 1977, Gutt 1988). A recent investigation of macrofauna associated with a number of Antarctic sponge species (Kunzmann, in press) shows that compared to demosponges, hexactinellida harbour an especially rich infauna. The reason for this lies in their overall morphology with a usually loose, easy-to-invade body structure and their vase- or sackshape, providing a large central cavity as living space. Bivalves, gastropods, polychaetes, several taxa of crustaceans and echinoderms dominate among the hexactinellid infauna. Kunzmann (loc. cit.) shows that there can be marked differences in the infauna community structure. In comparing the gross infauna composition (abundance) in the oscular cavity of the two closely related species *Rossella antarctica* and *R. racovitzae*, she shows that polychaetes dominate in *R. antarctica* (32.3%), while gastropods constitute the largest fraction in *R. racovitzae* (36.2%).

While many species of associated fauna are only found in low abundances, some occur in large numbers, and the habitat sponge can fulfill different functions for different associates. The size/frequency distribution of the amphipod *Seba antarctica* in the hexactinellid *Scolymastra joubini*, which consists of two distinct size classes even suggests the complete cycle of this species to take place in the sponge. In contrast, the specimens of asteroids and ophiuroids found in the central cavity of hexactinellids were usually small, juvenile stages. In these cases, hexactinellids seem to function as a sheltered kindergarden for young specimens of these species, protecting both against predation and transportation into unsuitable habitats.

The share of associated fauna that feeds on their host seems to be small. Kunzmann (loc. cit.) found spicule remnants in the stomachs of the gastropods *Trochaclis antarctica* and *Margarella* sp., in the nudibranch *Austrodoris kerguelensis*, well known to feed on sponges, and in the amphipods *Seba antarctica* and *Polycheria antarctica*. The most important predators identified in previous investigations are starfishes (*Perknaster fuscus antarcticus, Odontaster validus, O. meridionalis, Acodontaster conspicuus* and *A. hodgsoni*) and nudibranchs (e.g. *Austrodoris mcmurdensis*) (Dayton et al. 1974). While *P. fuscus antarcticus* has specialized on the demosponge *Mycale acerata*, this species is only a minor item in the diet of *A. conspicuus* and the nudibranch *A. mcmurdensis*, which feed predominantly on the three rossellids *Rossella racovitzae, R. nuda* and *Scolymastra joubini. O. meridionalis* and *A. hodgsoni* also include *R. racovitzae* in their diet, but prefer demosponges as food (Dayton et al. 1974). Smaller predators include diverse crustaceans like the amphipod *Echiniphimedia hodgsoni* (Coleman 1989). However, in the stomach of *E. hodgsoni*, only remnants of demosponges (presumably of the genera *Gellius*, *Hemigellius* or *Haliclona*) were found (Coleman 1989).

6. COLLECTION AND PRESERVATION

Hexactinellids are mostly found in deeper water and are thus as a rule collected with trawls and sledges. Only in the coastal waters of British Columbia and in the Antarctic they occur shallow enough to be collected by divers as well.

When collected by towed gear, hexactinellids should be sorted out from the catch immediately, to preserve good condition and to reduce their spicules tainting other dredged material. Special care has to be taken when trawls contain large amounts of demosponges; some Antarctic demosponge species, namely *Mycale acerata, Tedania vanhoeffeni* and *T. triraphis* exude enormous quantities of mucus difficult to remove from other objects.

In the fresh material, the following characteristics should be recorded before fixation: Dimensions, shape, presence of spicule root tuft, presence or absence of surface spiculation, colour - colours may change upon contact with air -, smell, consistency of tissue (soft, firm, resilient, easy to tear etc.), whether the specimen retained its body form or is collapsed, presence of buds, associated fauna.

For preservation, hexactinellids should be fixed in 4% borax buffered formaldehyde-seawater solution for at least one week but preferably not longer than 3 months. Afterwards they should be transferred to 80% alcohol. Between formaldehyde and alcohol, hexactinellids should at least be rinsed with tap water, preferably should they stand in tap water overnight to remove as much formaldehyde as possible. If not changed into alcohol, hexactinellids can disintegrate with time, even though they do not contain calcareous substance. Colour and texture of the hexactinellids after the different steps of preservation should ideally be recorded as well, as these informations are often contained in older literature and are important when comparing to material from previous collections. Another possibility is drying the material; this is best done after fixation with formaldehyde and rinsing with water. Dried specimens can easily be used for identification and especially in larger specimens drying reduces the weight problem considerably.

Spicule preparation for identification

Tissue samples for identification are best removed before fixation, but can be taken later as well. Pieces of about 0.25 cm^3 are usually large enough. As spiculation is different in different parts of the hexactinellid body, pieces of the interior and outer and inner surfaces of the body wall are necessary to get a good spicule complement. In some cases there are also special spicule types along the oscular rim and in the root tuft. These however can be plucked out of the specimens directly because of their enormous size. If the spicules are not prepared right away, the tissue samples can be frozen until needed. Drying is also possible, but samples should not be dried in an oven or a muffle furnace, as this can alter important details in the spicule shape.

Spicule preparation:

1. Transfer tissue sample into heat resistant test tube.

2. Add small quantity of concentrated nitric acid (fume hood) and heat to 70-80°C. Careful: cooking can be very violent! Dissolution of soft parts is over when red fumes are evaporated and the acid is clear again.

3. Let cool off; add absolute ethanole dropwise (!); cooking will begin anew. Careful: again cooking can be very violent, especially, if samples are not cooled off properly before adding the alcohol.

4. When cooking stops, add few more drops of alcohol. If cooking does not resume, add 1-2 ml ethanole and mix. Let stand for spicules to settle.

5. Remove acid/alcohol mixture carefully and replace by absolute ethanole.

6. Shake mixture to resuspend spicules; take them up with pipette and spread on slides. Light alcohol to burn. Permanent preparations can be made immediately, using DPX or similar embedding materials.

Note: Chemical reaction varies according to species, as does cooking time etc.. When spicules of a great size range are present, it is advisable to make separate preparations for separate size classes, i.e. remove large spicules first. In any case, 2-3 parallel slides from each spicule preparation are useful. Cooking of samples cut from specimens in formaldehyde is no problem, but alcohol preserved material is more difficult to prepare because of bad dissolution of tissue and violent cooking of the alcohol/acid mixture.

Material for histology

Material intended for electron microscopy can be prepared according to the method described by Mackie & Singla (1983), using a mixture of glutaraldehyde and osmium tetroxide for fixation. Material collected by divers is by far preferable, but trawled material can be used as well (Salomon & Barthel 1990).

7. Systematic Part

7.1 System of the Hexactinellida

The overall taxonomic system followed here is that of Ijima (1927), although somewhat simplified and with minor changes from Bergquist (1978), Burton (1929), Hartman (1982) and Lévi (1964).

Changes will be entered in the present hexactinellid system when with time a number of taxa have been revised or become better known through the appearence of new material. Because specialists are few and the existing material is scattered among many institutions it is impossible to foresee when this will happen. Meanwhile, Ijima's (loc. cit.) work is the latest comprehensive account of the group, and as such invaluable for hexactinellid workers at all levels. A most opportune and useful list of corrections to Ijima's "List of recognizably known recent hexactinellids arranged systematically" (loc. cit., p. 364-377) has been given by Reiswig (1990).

The identification of hexactinellid species relies at all taxonomic levels heavily on the types and dimensions of mega- and microscleres and on their positions and orientation in the sponge body. Important high level characters are the arrangement of the flagellated chambers, and if the megasclere hexactines are fused with each other by their rays or not. The last condition is normally easy to make out, although there are species where the degree of fusion is known to vary with the age of the specimens. At lower taxonomic levels the general bodyform, certain other details of the morphology of the specimens and the dimensions of some of the spicule types are considered distinctive. It should be kept in mind that gross morphology alone is highly unreliable for species determination.

7.2 CHECKLIST OF RECENT ANTARCTIC HEXACTINELLIDA

(Species recorded in Antarctica only from depths larger than 1000 meters are marked with an asterisk)

Class HEXACTINELLIDA

A. Subclass AMPHIDISCOPHORA

I. **Family Hyalonematidae**
 1. *Hyalonema (Cyliconema) drygalskii* *
 2. *Hyalonema* sp. *

B. Subclass HEXASTEROPHORA
 a. Order DICTYONINA

II. **Family Farreidae**
 3. *Farrea occa*

III. **Family Euretidae**
 4. *Pararete gerlachei*

IV. **Family Coscinoporidae**
 5. *Chonelasma lamella*
 6. *Bathyxiphus* sp. *

V. **Family Aulocalycidae**
 7. *Aulocalyx irregularis* *

b. Order LYSSACINOSA

VI. **Family Euplectellidae**
 8. *Holascus tenuis* *
 9. *Holascus obesus* *
 10. *Malacosaccus coatsi* *
 11. *Malacosaccus pedunculatus* *
 12. *Acoelocalyx brucei**
 13. *Docosaccus ancoratus**

VII. Family Caulophacidae
14. *Caulophacus valdiviae* *
15. *Caulophacus antarcticus* *
16. *Caulophacus scotiae* *
17. *Caulophacus instabilis* *

VIII. Family Rossellidae
18. *Rossella antarctica*
19. *Rossella racovitzae*
20. *Rossella villosa*
21. *Rossella fibulata*
22. *Rossella nuda*
23. *Rossella levis*
24. *Rossella vanhoeffeni*
25. *Bathydorus spinosus*
26. *Calycosoma validum* *
27. *Anoxycalyx ijimai*
28. *Scolymastra joubini*

7.3 KEY TO THE SUBCLASSES AND FAMILIES KNOWN FROM ANTARCTICA

1a   With amphidiscs, without hexasters ....
        subclass AMPHIDISCOPHORA; family Hyalonematidae p. 51
1b   With hexasters, without amphidiscs ....
        .... subclass HEXASTEROPHORA 2
2a(1b) Large hexactines fused into rigid framework; uncinates mostly
        present, no rhabd-shaped diactines (order DICTYONINA) 3
2b   Large hexactines commonly free, but can be rigidly connected;
        rhabd-shaped diactines present, no uncinates (order LYSSA-
        CINOSA) 6
3a(2a) Loose, 200-300 μm long club- or anchorshaped spicules present;
        main skeleton in one layer .... family **Farreidae** p. 55
3b   Loose, 200-400 μm long forkshaped spicules present, or such a
        category lacking; main skeleton in more layers 4
4a(3b) The skeleton meshes irregularly shaped and varying much in
        dimensions (bigger ones being 2-3 times larger than the smaller
        ones); the skeleton hexactines with curved prolonged (longer than
        mesh side) rays; no forkshaped spicules; no uncinates ....
        .... family **Aulocalycidae** p. 66
4b   The skeleton meshes regularly triangular or quadrangular, all of
        about the same size; the skeleton hexactines with straight rays
        usually not longer than the side of the mesh; forkshaped spicules
        usually present 5
5a(4b) Body tubular, branching and anastomosing; body wall simple,
        without cavities larger than the meshes; forkshaped spicules pre-
        sent .... family **Euretidae** p. 58
5b   Body cup- or plateshaped; bodywall with numerous fun-
        nelshaped, blind-ending cavities, larger than the meshes; fork-
        shaped spicules usually present ..... family **Coscinoporidae** p. 60
6a(2b) The spicules of the outer dermal layer are large (up to 1 mm long)
        sword-shaped hexactines, with the long ray oriented inwards; no
        hypodermal spicules .... family **Euplectellidae** p. 69
6b   The spicules of the outer dermal layer are smaller (at most up to
        0.5 mm long) spined hexactines, pentactines or tetractines; mostly
        with a hypodermal layer of large spicules, always pentactines,
        sometimes also diactines 7

7a(6b) Body mushroom- or cupshaped, on cylindrical tubular stalk; dermal spicules hexactines (on the stalk sometimes pentactines); the hypodermal spicules are pentactines with the paired rays in or just below the surface .... family **Caulophacidae** p. 78

7b Body cup- or sackshaped, sometimes stalked; surface spicules are rough pentactines or tetractines with the rays in one plane, rarely hexactines; the hypodermal pentactines can be either lacking, rare or numerous; they sometimes protrude outwards to such a degree that their paired rays are lifted far over the surface and form a veil-like structure .... family **Rossellidae** p. 86

7.4 Subclass AMPHIDISCOPHORA Schulze, 1886

Diagnosis: Hexactinellida with amphidiscs as microscleres. Hexasters do not occur.

The wall megascleres are free hexactines, some of them often with reduced number of rays. Inner and outer dermal spicules are pentactines with the unpaired ray pointing distally. Hypodermal spicules are large pentactines with the unpaired ray directed into the wall.

The species are soft bottom inhabitants, rooted by means of special long anchoring spicules, either arranged in a compact stalk or in one or more tufts.

7.4.1 Family Hyalonematidae Gray, 1857

Diagnosis: Amphidiscophora with well delimited, apical oscular area, which may be covered by a sievelike membrane. Most of the wall skeleton hexactines reduced to diactines. With a compact basal twisted stalk consisting of a bunch of anchoring spicules that continue into the body as a central columella.

Genus HYALONEMA Gray, 1832

Remarks: This is the only genus of the family HYALONEMATIDAE represented in Antarctica. *Hyalonema* comprises about 100 nominal species that all live in the deep-sea, and has been divided into 14 subgenera (Lendenfeld 1915, Ijima 1927). One species and a single record referable to the genus are known from Antarctica. Two other species, *H. (Corynonema) clavigerum* Schulze, 1886 and *H. (Coscinonema) conus* Schulze, 1886, have been recorded just outside the considered area.

52

Hyalonema (Cyliconema) drygalskii Schulze & Kirkpatrick, 1910
Figure 10

Hyalonema drygalskii Schulze & Kirkpatrick, 1910 a: 293-295;
b: 7-10, pl. 10 figs. 1-1w.

Description: The oval body is up to 18 mm long, and 11 mm in diameter, on an 11 mm long stalk. The oscule is about 2 mm in diameter and provided with a 1 mm high fringe of protruding diactines. Distinguishing characters of the species are small size of the largest category of amphidiscs (95 - 110 μm), the fact that the inner dermal skeleton consists solely of diactines, and that the wall skeleton contains very few diactines.

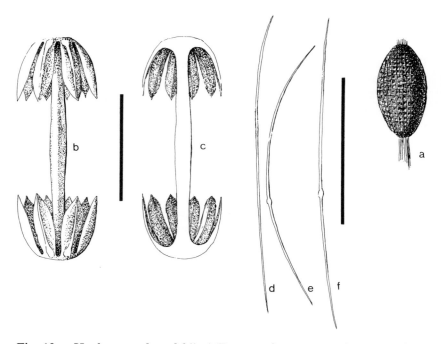

Fig. 10: *Hyalonema drygalskii.* a) Type specimen, somewhat more than 1.4 times natural size; b) large amphidisc, scale bar 50 μm; c) same spicule in median section; d, e, f) different types of inner dermal diactines, scale bar 500 μm. After Schulze & Kirkpatrick (1910b; plate 10).

Distribution: The only known specimen was found off Wilhelm II Land, at 2725 m depth.

Hyalonema sp., Topsent 1913 (1920): 608-609.

Description: A 5 cm long fragment of a stalk with some tissues from the body at one end.

Distribution: One locality in the eastern Weddell Sea, at 2580 m depth.

Remarks: Topsent (loc. cit.) with hesitation compared the fragment to *H. (Leptonema) ovuliferum* Schulze, 1899 and *H. (Leptonema) urna* Schulze, 1904. Identity with *H. drygalskii* cannot at present be excluded, but some differences in types of spicules present and in their dimensions seem to be found.

7.5 Subclass HEXASTEROPHORA Schulze, 1886

Diagnosis: Hexactinellida with hexasters as microscleres. Amphidiscs do not occur.

The wall hexactines may be free or fused together by their rays into a rigid skeleton network. The inner and outer dermal spicules can be hexactine, pentactine or diactine. If the distally pointing ray is found, these spicules are normally hexactine. Where a hypodermal skeleton exists it consists of either pentactines or diactines. Hexasters are found in numerous variations in size, morphology and position.

The species are generally hardbottom inhabitants, fixed firmly at the base. A small number of species live on soft bottom, rooted by anchoring spicules.

7.5.1 Order DICTYONINA Zittel, 1877

Diagnosis: Hexasterophora with fused main skeleton, consisting solely of hexactines.

Members of this order are always firmly attached to some kind of substrate. The early stage seems in all cases to be cupshaped. With later growth the body can take different forms, more or less regarded characteristic for whole genera.

The body wall skeleton is coherent, rather rigid, formed by the fusion of the rays of large hexactines. Most often the rays lie parallel to each other and fuse in their whole length, thus forming a regular structure. In a few genera the hexactines lie disordered in relation to each other, and the skeleton meshes are of varying dimensions and of irregular form. The fused skeletons can consist of one or more layers of hexactines. On the free outer and inner sides of the skeleton, the nonfused rays are protruding as large spines. Both the skeleton and the free rays can be rough or covered with small spines. There is an outer and an inner dermal skeleton consisting of loose megascleres, in most cases pentactines. There is always a number of loose spicules of various categories, somewhat different from genus to genus; they comprise small hexactines, uncinates, club-, anchor-, or forkshaped spicules, and various forms of hexasters, most commonly oxyhexasters and/or discohexasters.

The skeleton can attain different degrees of complexity. In the simplest form the only passages for water are the ordinary skeleton meshes with the sidelength usually not exceeding the length of the hexactine rays. In more complicated skeletons a pattern of spaces of much greater dimension than the meshside length is formed during growth in connection with a more complicated water transport system. Sometimes they are not readily seen, because they become covered by the dermal skeleton layers. In a number of species a folding of the whole bodywall creates alternating external and internal groves, strongly influencing the gross morphology.

7.5.1.1 Family Farreidae Schulze, 1886

Diagnosis: Body composed of tubes, either single or branched and anastomosing, all of about the same diameter, and with each terminal part ending with an osculum. The skeleton is simple, generally with

Fig. 11: *Farrea occa*. Dictyonine skeleton; the upper side is the outer side, the lower the inner; scale bar 500 μm. After Schulze (1887, plate 71, *F. haeckeli*).

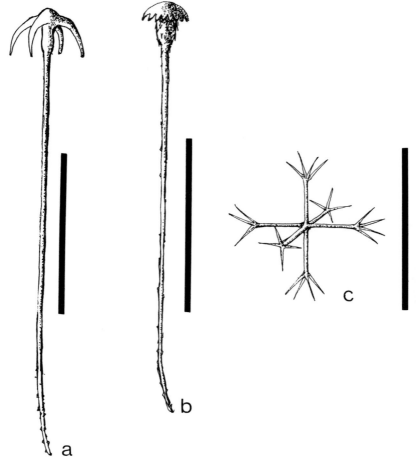

Fig. 12:   *Farrea occa.* a) anchorshaped dermal spicule, scale bar 100 μm; b) clubshaped dermal spicule, scale bar 100 μm; c) oxyhexaster, scale bar 100 μm. After Schulze (1887, plate 71, *F. haeckeli*).

quadrangular meshes with the side length equal to the ray length of the hexasters. Club- and anchorshaped spicules always present.

Genus FARREA Bowerbank, 1862

Diagnosis: As that of the family.

Remarks: This is the only genus of the family FARREIDAE represented in Antarctica. *Farrea* comprises about 15 species. The type species, *F. occa*, is the one most often reported, and is the only one recorded from the Antarctic area. It has been divided into about 10 subspecies (Ijima 1927) the validity of which seems questionable; the subspecies are not taken into consideration here.

Farrea occa Bowerbank, 1862
Figures 2b, 11, 12

Farrea occa Topsent 1901: 7, 1902: 38.

Diagnosis: The body is a dichotomously branching network of round tubes, which are up to 15 mm in diameter. It is attached by a tubular stalk with compact, expanded base. The maximum dimension of the body is at least up to 12 cm, but most samples consist of fragments.

The tube wall is supported by a singlelayered rigid, although somewhat elastic, framework of hexactines which have their rays fused into a very regular quadrangular network, with the mesh side the length of one ray. From each node in the network large free microspined rays project both outwards and inwards. In older specimens the framework can consist of two layers in the lowermost part.

Besides the fused hexactines, the skeleton comprises dermal outer and inner pentactines, loose, 200 - 300 μm long, club- or anchorshaped outer and inner dermal spicules, long uncinates, and oxyhexasters.

Distribution: *Farrea occa* is found worldwide, in depths of 200-1900 m. In Antarctica it has been found in the Bellingshausen Sea at 450 m, and the eastern Weddell Sea at 2000 m. In the last case, the material may originate from shallower depth since it consisted of unattached skeletons without soft parts.

7.5.1.2 Family Euretidae Schulze, 1886

Diagnosis: The body consists of dichotomously branching and anastomosing tubes, which mostly form an irregular network. The skeletal network consists of more than one layer of fused hexactines, forming triangular or somewhat irregular meshes, which are all of about the same size (Fig. 6).

Genus PARARETE Ijima, 1927

Diagnosis: The body consists of branching and anastomosing tubules. Outer and inner dermal skeleton consist of pentactines. The only microsclere category is discohexasters.

Remarks: This is the only genus of the family so far recorded from the Antarctic area. Because the limits of the genera within the Euretidae are poorly defined, the number of species in each genus is somewhat uncertain, but at least seven are at present listed under the name of *Pararete*. One species has been recorded from Antarctica.

Pararete gerlachei (Topsent, 1901)
Figure 13

Eurete gerlachei Topsent, 1901: 7; 1902: 38-40, pl. 2, fig. 4, pl. 5, figs. 2-9.

Diagnosis: Only known as fragments that seem to come from a branched tubular body. The tubes measure 8-10 mm in diameter, with up to 2 mm thick wall.

The fused skeleton has rather irregular meshes on the outside of the tubes and more regular, often nearly rectangular, on the inside. The hexactines on the outer side are more robust than those on inner side. There are numerous spined oxyhexactines of varying sizes; some are free and some are loosely attached to the meshes of the main skeleton, sometimes to such a degree as to form a kind of incomplete secondary skeleton. Other free spicules are outer and inner dermal rough pentactines, uncinates, about 400 μm long forkshaped spicules with mostly five or six slender arms each ending in a small knob, and discohexasters about 65 μm in diameter.

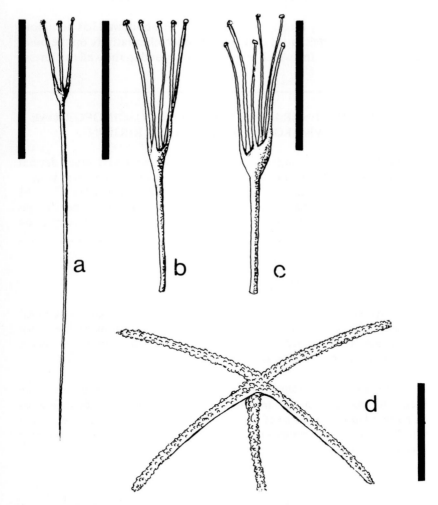

Fig. 13: *Pararete gerlachei*. a, b, c) forkshaped spicules; scale bars: a) 100 μm, b and c) 50 μm; d) outer dermal pentactine, scale bar 200 μm. Redrawn after Topsent (1902, plate 5, *Eurete gerlachei*).

Distribution: The species has been recorded from three localities in the Bellingshausen Sea, at depths of 450-550 m.

7.5.1.3 Family Coscinoporidae Zittel, 1877

Diagnosis: The body is cup- or plateshaped. The bodywall has numerous blind-ending, funnelshaped cavities, that open alternatively on the outer and inner surfaces, and which in length correspond to the wall thickness.

KEY TO THE GENERA AND SPECIES OF COSCINOPORIDAE KNOWN FROM THE ANTARCTIC REGION

1a   Body cupshaped; wall up to 6 mm thick; outer and inner dermal spicules are pentactines with the unpaired ray pointing inwards .... *Chonelasma lamella* p. 61

1b   Body of a sword-like shape, up to 3 mm thick; outer and inner dermal spicules are hexactines with spined distal ray .. *Bathyxiphus* sp. p. 64

Genus CHONELASMA Schulze, 1886

Diagnosis: Body cupshaped, maybe platelike in some species. The fused skeleton very regular. Dermal spicules pentactines or hexactines with spined rays. Fork-shaped spicules, uncinates and discohexasters always occur, and sometimes other kinds of hexasters and small hexactines.

Remarks: The genus comprises 5-6 species, mostly from deep water. The literature contains many records that could only be identified as "*Chonelasma* sp.", because of easy fragmentation and abrasion (e.g. Topsent 1913). The only species known from Antarctica is *C. lamella*, the type species.

61

Chonelasma lamella Schulze, 1886
Figures 14, 15, 16, plates I, II

Chonelasma lamella Schulze 1887: 321-323, pl. 87, figs. 1-2, pl. 88, figs. 1-9.
Chonelasma lamella choanoides Schulze & Kirkpatrick, 1910a: 302; 1910b: 48-53, pl. 8, figs. 1-5, pl. 10, figs. 2-2g.
Chonelasma sp., Topsent 1901: 7; 1902: 40, pl. 1, fig. 8, pl. 5, figs. 10-11.
Uncinatera plicata Topsent, 1901: 7-8; 1902: 41-43, pl. 2, fig. 7, figs. 10-12, pl. 6, figs. 1-10.

Diagnosis: Presumably cupshaped, up to 7 cm in diameter and about 10 cm high. A stemlike part is up to 2 cm in diameter and 3 cm high, with a basal plate. The wall thickness is 5-10 mm. The central cavity continues down to the basal plate.

The fused skeleton is regular, with large meshes in the interior of the wall, and smaller and somewhat irregular meshes close to the outer and inner surfaces. The outer and inner dermal skeleton consists of strong pentactines oriented with the unpaired ray inwards. The pentactines are spined, the four rays in the dermal surfaces only on their outer side. Between the pentactines are forked spicules mostly with four branches. Other spicules, found in the interior of the wall, are uncinates, oxyhexactines, oxyhexasters, discohexactines and discohexasters, the four last categories of about the same size, 100-120 μm in diameter.

Distribution: In Antarctica *C. lamella* is known from localities in the Bellingshausen Sea, the eastern Weddell Sea, off Wilhelm II Land and near Crozet Islands, thus probably being circumantarctic in distribution (Fig. 16). The depths varied from 430-3397 m, with the shallowest, 430-500 m, in the Bellingshausen Sea. Living specimens were only taken at about 450 m, and outside the Antarctic region at about 1000 m; all deeper records represent macerated, even mudfilled skeleton remains that can have been transported down. Outside Antarctica the species is known from the South Pacific and possibly from the North Atlantic.

Remarks: Because the mid-wall part of the fused skeleton is rather weak in construction, fragments often split into two flakes, one representing the outer half, the other the inner half of the wall, and identification can be difficult if this kind of fragment by mistake is considered to represent a full wall skeleton section; in case of doubt, one should look for the presence of a subdermal skeleton on both sides of the fragment. The diameter of the microscleres in Antarctic specimens may be somewhat smaller than given above.

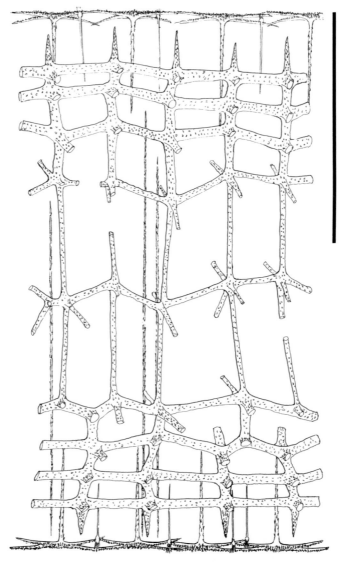

Fig. 14: *Chonelasma lamella*. Dictyonine skeleton, scale bar 2 mm. After Schulze (1887, plate 88).

Genus BATHYXIPHUS Schulze, 1899

Diagnosis: The body has the form of a sword-blade, up to more than 14 cm long, 10 mm wide and 5 mm thick. It is fixed to the substrate by a rounded basal plate, at least 2 cm in diameter and 3 mm thick.

Remarks: The genus comprises only the type species *B. subtilis* Schulze, 1899 (Fig. 17). Abraided fragments that could be referred to the genus have been recorded from several localities in the Pacific, in the Atlantic Ocean and in the Antarctic. The type specimen came from a depth of 1250 m; all deeper records are dead skeleton parts, and the fact that most of them are stated to come from soft bottom even if they have the basal plate points to the possibility that they can have been transported down.

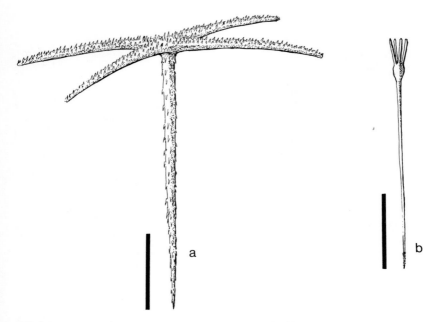

Fig. 15:   *Chonelasma lamella.* a) dermal pentactine, scale bar 100 μm; b) forkshaped spicule, scale bar 100 μm. After Schulze (1887, plate 88).

Bathyxiphus sp., Schulze & Kirkpatrick 1910: 53-56, pl. 9, figs. 6-15, pl. 10, figs. 3-3c.

Description: A number of skeletons devoid of soft parts and loose spicules were placed in the genus, mostly because of the characteristic bodyform. They were with hesitation referred to *B. subtilis.*
Distribution: specimens were found at three localities off Wilhelm II Land, at depths of 2450-3397 m.

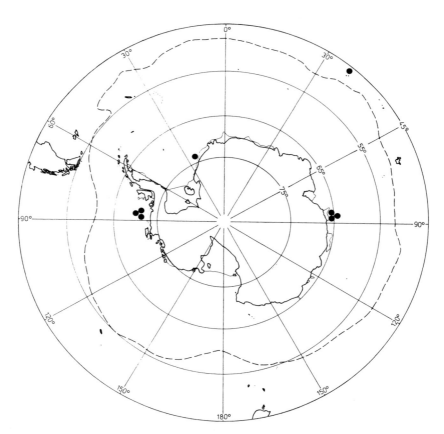

Fig. 16:   Antarctic distribution of *Chonelasma lamella.*

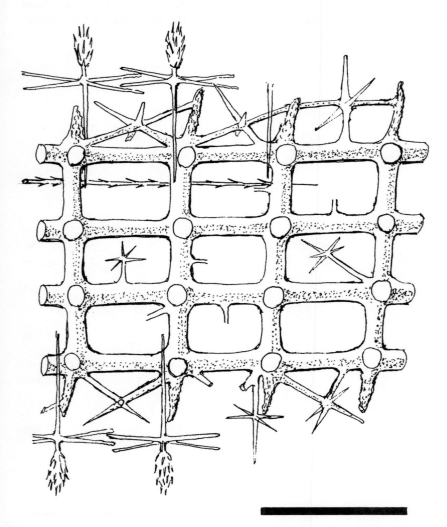

Fig. 17: *Batyxiphus subtilis*. Dictyonine skeleton, scale bar 500 μm.
After Schulze (1899, plate 17).

7.5.1.4 Family Aulocalycidae Ijima, 1927

Diagnosis: The body is cup- or tubeshaped. The skeletal framework with meshes of undefined shape, which vary much in dimensions. The arrangement of the skeletal hexactines is exceedingly irregular; they have greatly prolonged, curved rays that meet each other and fuse at various angles.

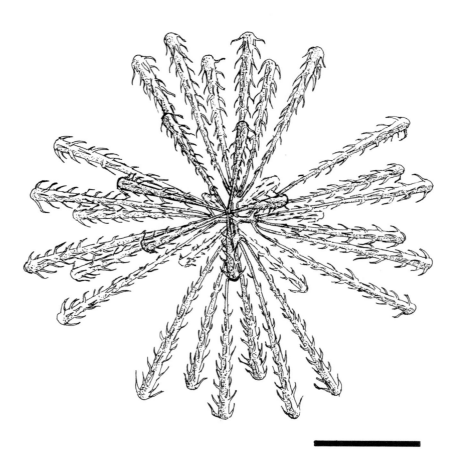

Fig. 18: *Aulocalyx irregularis.* Large hexaster, scale bar 100 μm. After Schulze (1887, plate 60).

Genus AULOCALYX Schulze, 1886

Diagnosis: Bodywall with longitudinal folds; oscular cavity well developed. With characteristic, large hexasters, 300-400 μm in diameter, that have very long clubshaped appendages, beset with numerous recurved spines. No uncinates.

Remarks: The genus comprises two rarely encountered species, one of which has been recorded a number of times in or near to Antarctica.

Aulocalyx irregularis Schulze, 1886
Figures 18, 19

Aulocalyx irregularis Schulze, 1886: 56; 1887: 174-176, pl. 60, figs. 1-5. Schulze & Kirkpatrick 1910: 58, pl. 8, fig. 6.

Description: A number of up to 5 cm large, hard skeletal fragments that seem to originate from a cupshaped body with a basal plate.

Distribution: *A. irregularis* is known from off Wilhelm II Land at 3397 m, from between Marion and Crozet Islands at 2928 m, and off Prince Edwards Island from 567 m depth (Fig. 19).

Remarks: The species is poorly known, having been recorded only as fragmented skeletons. Remains of soft parts were found only in the sample from the shallowest locality, so there is the possibility that the deep records are in reality downtransported skeletons.

7.5.2 Order LYSSACINOSA Ijima, 1927

Diagnosis: The main skeleton normally consisting of free megascleres, although some degree of fusion is known in some species. Megascleres basically hexactines, often with some reduction in the number of rays. Diactines always present, in some cases dominating. Uncinates do not occur.

Members of the order are generally cup- or sackshaped or tubular with broad basis or stalk. They are either cemented to some kind of hard substrate or rooted in loose bottom by the stalk, by fingerlike extensions from the basal part or by long spicule tufts.

The inner and outer dermal skeletons consist of hexactines or pentactines. These are rather large (up to 1 mm length) if there is no hypodermal skeleton. If a hypodermal skeleton is developed, it consists of large pentactines with the unpaired ray pointing inwards, and sometimes also bundles of diactines; in this case the dermal skeleton spicules are smaller (up to 0.5 mm length).

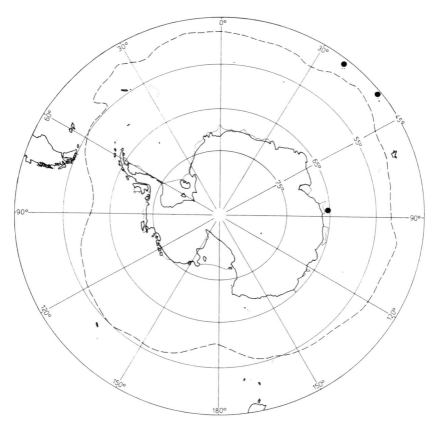

Fig. 19: Antarctic distribution of *Aulocalyx irregularis*.

7.5.2.1 Family Euplectellidae Gray 1867 sensu Ijima 1903

Diagnosis: Tubular, cupformed or massive body, sometimes stalked. Either fixed with a long tuft of spicules with anchorshaped distal ends, or attached by a more compact base. Outer dermal skeleton of large sword-shaped hexactines with the prolonged ray pointing inwards. No hypodermal skeleton. Inner dermal skeleton spicules with rays varying in number from six to two.

KEY TO THE GENERA AND SPECIES OF EUPLECTELLIDAE
KNOWN FROM THE ANTARCTIC REGION

1a   Body tubular, with a sieve plate .... *Holascus* 5
1b   Body not tubular, no sieve plate 2
2a(1b)   Body not stalked; body wall at most 2 mm thick ....
.... *Docosaccus ancoratus* p. 76
2b   Body stalked; body wall 4 - 15 mm thick 3
3a(2b)   Body very soft, oblong and flattened, with shallow inner cavity; no floricomes .... *Acoelocalyx brucei* p. 76
3b   Body oblong, with deep inner cavity, floricomes present 4
4a(3b)   Floricomes about 110 μm in diameter; inner dermal skeleton of hexactines .... *Malacosaccus coatsi* p. 74
4b   Floricomes about 145 μm in diameter; inner dermal skeleton mostly of pentactines .... *Malacosaccus pedunculatus* p. 74
5a(1a)   Bodywall 1 - 1.5 mm thick; besides oxyhexasters, 2-3 types of hexasters with split ends, measuring 100 μm (calycocomes), 300-350 μm (calycocomes), and 400-500 μm (graphiocomes) in diameter .... *Holascus tenuis* p. 71
5b   Bodywall about 3 mm thick; besides oxyhexasters, only one type of hexaster with split ends, measuring 400-500 μm (graphiocomes) in diameter .... *Holascus obesus* p. 72

Genus HOLASCUS Schulze, 1886

Diagnosis: The tubular body has a well defined sieve plate covering the osculum, and is fastened with a spicule tuft. The outer surface is nearly smooth, while the inner has longitudinal and transverse ridges forming a regular latticework. The wall skeleton is organized into a network consisting of the greatly prolonged rays of hexactines or pentactines.

Remarks: No hexasters of the floricome-type. The genus contains 10 species, all from the deep-sea. Two are found in Antarctica, and two, *H. fibulatus* Schulze, 1886 and *H. polajevi* Schulze, 1886, just outside the considered area.

Fig. 20: *Holascus tenuis*. Habitus, about 1.1 times natural size. After Schulze (1904, plate 1).

Holascus tenuis Schulze, 1904
Figures 20, 21

Holascus tenuis Schulze, 1904: 3-7, pl. 1, figs. 1-14.

Description: The tubular body is 75 mm long and 7 mm in diameter. The tubewall is 1-1.5 mm thick. The outer surface a little rough from small conules, the inner surface nearly smooth. The basal end with bundles of spicules forming a tuft, about 20 mm long.

The main skeleton consists of large pentactines, which are arranged with the one spiny ray outwards and the four smooth rays prolonged in the plane of the bodywall in a pattern so they form a regular quadrangular network.

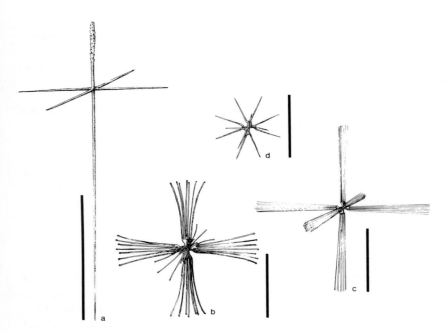

Fig. 21:   *Holascus tenuis.* a) hypodermal hexactine, scale bar 1 mm; b) large subdermal calycocome; c) graphiocome; d) oxyhexaster; scale bars b-d) 150 μm. After Schulze (1904, plate 1).

72

The loose spicules are diactines, some triactines, and hexasters formed as oxyhexasters, graphiocomes and calycocomes.

Distribution: The species has been recorded once, off Enderbyland at 4636 m depth.

Remarks: The two known specimens were both rather worn.

Holascus obesus Schulze, 1904

Holascus obesus Schulze, 1904: 7-8, pl. 1, figs. 15-18.

Description: The tubular body can be at least 50 mm long, and is 10 mm in diameter. The tubewall is 3 mm thick. The outer surface is uneven, the inner surface is even and velvetlike.

The main skeleton consists of large pentactines, with one spiny ray pointing outwards and the four smooth rays prolonged in the bodywall plane.

Loose spicules are diactines, triactines, and hexasters formed as oxyhexasters and graphiocomes.

Distribution: The single known fragment was recorded off Enderby Land, at a depth of 4636 m.

Remarks: The species is known only from a somewhat abraided fragment without basal tuft of anchoring spicules. The characters for distinguishing the species are the lack of calycocomes, and perhaps the uneven texture of the outer surface, which is elsewise not found in the genus.

Genus MALACOSACCUS Schulze, 1886

Diagnosis: The stalked sack- or tubeshaped body is rather soft, with the outer surface uniformly even, and the inner surface with larger or smaller irregularly distributed openings. The main skeleton consists of several layers of hexactines with long, flexible rays that, apposed loosely to each other, form a network with cubic meshes. Microscleres are oxyhexasters, discohexasters and floricomes.

Remarks: The genus contains 6 deep-sea species, two of which are found in the Antarctic, and one, *M. vastus* Schulze, 1886 has been taken just outside the considered area.

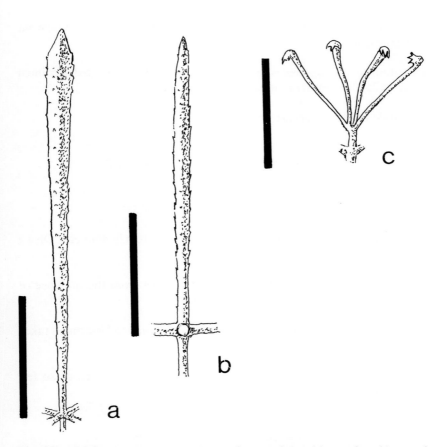

Fig. 22:   *Malacosaccus coatsi*. a) ray of outer dermal hexactine; b) ray of inner dermal hexactine; scale bars a,b) 100 μm; c) ray of floricome-like hexaster, scale bar 50 μm. After Topsent (1913, plate 6).

Malacosaccus coatsi Topsent, 1910
Figure 22

Malacosaccus coatsi Topsent, 1910: 3-5; 1913 (1920): 588-592, pl. 2, figs. 4-5, pl. 6, fig. 1.

Description: Cupshaped on stalk, at least 9 cm high and 7 cm in diameter. The very soft bodywall is folded at least at the base and is up to 15 mm thick. The inner cavity may be narrow. Stalk 3-7 cm thick and up to about 40 cm long, massive.

The main skeleton is typical for the genus. The discohexasters somewhat resemble floricomes.

Distribution: The species is known from one heavily damaged specimen taken at 2580 m depth in the eastern Weddell Sea.

Remarks: Oxyhexasters are few.

Malacosaccus pedunculatus Topsent, 1910
Fig. 23

Malacosaccus pedunculatus Topsent, 1910: 1-3; 1913 (1920): 584-587.

Description: Cupshaped, about 14 cm high and 6-9 cm in diameter. On a 3 mm thick and 10 cm long massive flexible stalk.

The main skeleton is typical for the genus, apart from the presence of areas with pentactines in the inner dermal layer.

Distribution: The species is known from one fragmented specimen taken at 2580 m depth in the eastern Weddell Sea.

Remarks: The species perhaps lacks oxyhexasters altogether, as so few were found in the material that they may be foreign.

Genus ACOELOCALYX Topsent, 1910

Diagnosis: The slender, compressed body is very soft and with only a shallow inner cavity. Long, stiff, cylindrical stalk that carries a short spicule tuft at the lower end. The skeleton network consists of irregularly distributed hexactines with thin, long, flexible rays. Microscleres are oxyhexasters and discohexasters.

Remarks: The genus contains only one species.

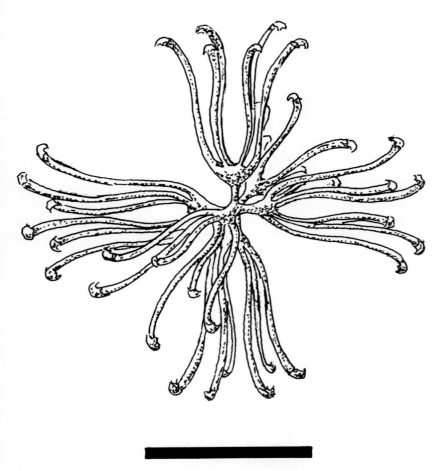

Fig. 23: *Malacosaccus vastus*. Floricome, typical of the genus; scale bar 50 µm. After Schulze (1887, plate 18). Note: There exist no original drawings on the species *M. pedunculatus*.

Acoelocalyx brucei Topsent, 1910
Figure 24

Acoelocalyx brucei Topsent, 1910: 5-8; 1913 (1920): 592-595, pl. 1, figs. 1-2, pl. 6., fig 4.

Description: As the genus. The 15 cm long, flattened body is 23-44 mm wide and 10-8 mm thick, being thinner towards the upper end. It is on a 6 mm thick and 22 cm long, massive stalk with a 4 cm long spicule tuft at the lower end.

Distribution: The only known specimen was taken at 4547 m depth in the northern Weddell Sea.

Remarks: In the original description it is not stated that the stalk is massive, but it is implied.

Genus DOCOSACCUS Topsent, 1910

Diagnosis: Body supposedly sackshaped with thin, stiff walls and fixed by one or more spicule tufts. The main skeleton hexactines are of two size categories, the smaller type often reduced to diactines, the larger nearly to tetractines. Microscleres are oxyhexasters, discohexasters and floricomes.

Remarks: The genus contains only one species.

Docosaccus ancoratus Topsent, 1910
Figure 25

Docosaccus ancoratus Topsent, 1910: 8-10; 1913 (1920): 595-598, pl. 3, fig. 4, pl. 6., fig. 6.

Description: As for the genus. Known only as fragments, the largest of which measures 4x4 cm and is 2 mm thick. The small category of hexactines forms a network, while the large category which gives the wall the stiffness shows no regularity in position.

Distribution: The only known specimen was taken at 4547 m depth in the central Weddell Sea.

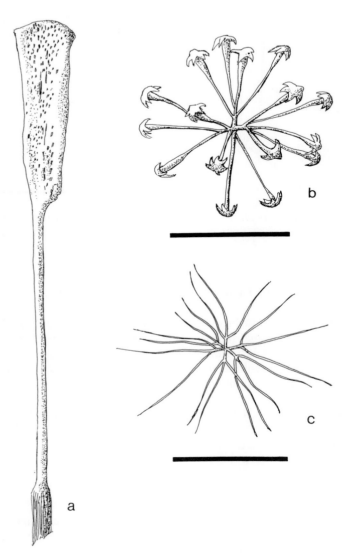

Fig. 24: *Acoelocalyx brucei*. a) habitus, about one third original size; b) discohexaster, scale bar 100 μm; c) oxyhexaster, scale bar 100 μm. After Topsent (1913, plates 1 and 6).

78

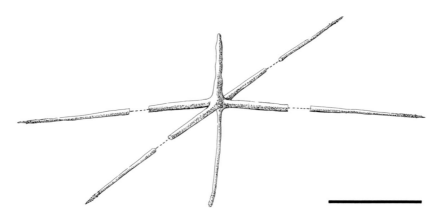

Fig. 25: *Docosaccus ancoratus*. Large hexactine; the shortest ray points away from the sponge surface; scale bar 1 mm. Redrawn after Topsent (1913, plate 6).

7.5.2.2 Family Caulophacidae Ijima, 1903

Diagnosis: Cup- or mushroomshaped body that is stalked and firmly attached at base. Dermal skeleton of small hexactines supported by large hypodermal pentactines. Main skeleton of hexactines and diactines. There are loose discohexactines and as microscleres discohexasters, sometimes including plumicomes.

Remarks: Only one genus, *Caulophacus,* is known from Antarctica. A representative of the genus *Sympagella*, *S. johnstoni* (Schulze, 1886), has been found just outside the considered area.

Genus CAULOPHACUS Schulze, 1886

Diagnosis: Cup- or mushroomshaped, on a long stalk which usually has a central narrow canal. Discohexactines and discohexasters present in various types but no plumicomes.

Remarks: The upper convex side of the mushroom-shaped specimens represents the inner dermal surface of cupshaped specimens of other genera, while the lower, often concave side represents the outer dermal surface. Fifteen deep-water species have been referred to *Caulophacus*, and the literature further contains a number of records just given as *Caulophacus* sp. Four species are found in the Antarctic area, whereas 2 more have been taken just outside the considered area (*C. latus* Schulze, 1886; *C. pipetta* Schulze, 1886)

KEY TO THE SPECIES OF CAULOPHACUS KNOWN FROM THE ANTARCTIC REGION

1a   Inner dermal/upper skeleton mostly pentactines with a knob in place of the reduced ray (Fig. 28a) 2
1b   Inner/upper dermal skeleton mostly hexactines 3
2a(1a) Inner dermal pentactines with about 300 μm long and 10 μm thick distal ray, covered with small spines except for part of the very tip (Fig. 28a) .... *C. valdiviae* p. 79
2b   Inner dermal pentactines with 220 μm long and up to 25 μm thick distal ray, covered with small spines that are gradually more numerous towards the distal end (Fig. 29c) .... *C. antarcticus* p. 80
3a(1b) Some discohexasters more than 150 μm, up to 330 μm in diameter .... *C. scotiae* p. 83
3b   Discohexasters less than 150 μm in diameter ..... *C. instabilis* p. 85

Caulophacus valdiviae Schulze, 1904
Figures 26, 27, 28

Caulophacus valdiviae Schulze, 1904: 25-28, pl. 6, figs. 1-16.

Description: The species is mushroom-shaped. The body is flat to convex, about 10 cm in diameter and up to 1 cm thick. It is on a round, massive, up to 4 cm long and 3-10 mm thick, somwhat bent stalk with an attachment plate at the lower, thin end. In the main skeleton hexactines and hypodermal pentactines, the spinulation of the rays has a characteristic distribution, as it covers the tip and a belt in the middle part. There are discohexactines, 180-190 μm in diameter, and discohexasters, about 100 μm in diameter.

Distribution: Several specimens were taken at 4636 m depth off Enderby Land. Fragments that may belong to this species were recorded at 450 m in the Bellingshausen Sea.

Remarks: Schulze & Kirkpatrick (1910b) pointed to the possible identity of a *Caulophacus* sp. mentioned by Topsent (1901, 1902) with *C. valdiviae*.

Caulophacus antarcticus Schulze & Kirkpatrick, 1910
Figure 29

Caulophacus antarcticus Schulze & Kirkpatrick, 1910a: 295-296; 1910b: 10-13, pl. 1, figs. 1-1h, pl. 9, figs. 1-5.

Description: Bodyform unknown. The hollow cylindrical stem is up to 21 cm long and 12 mm in diameter. The lower part is often sharply bent and has a basal attachment plate. The wall skeleton arrangement is not

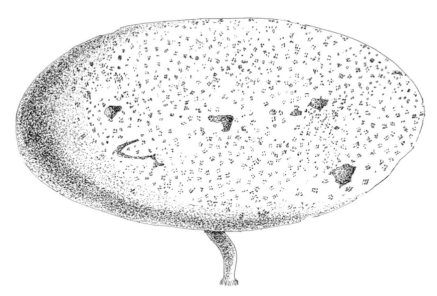

Fig. 26: *Caulophacus valdiviae*. Habitus, about 1.2 times original size. Redrawn after Schulze (1904, plate 6).

known. The supposed inner dermal pentactines have a characteristically spined distal ray. There are finely spined small oxyhexactines, discohexactines and discohexasters.

Distribution: Stalks of a number of specimens were found at three localities off Wilhelm II Land, at depths of 2450 - 3397 m.

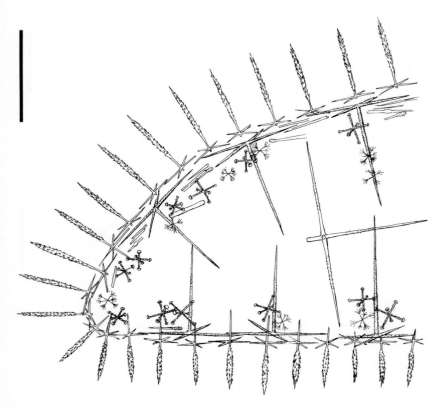

Fig. 27: *Caulophacus valdiviae*. Skeletal arrangement. The upper side represents the inner, the lower side the outer dermal skeleton; scale bar about 500 μm; note: spicules are not drawn exactly to scale. After Schulze (1904, plate 6).

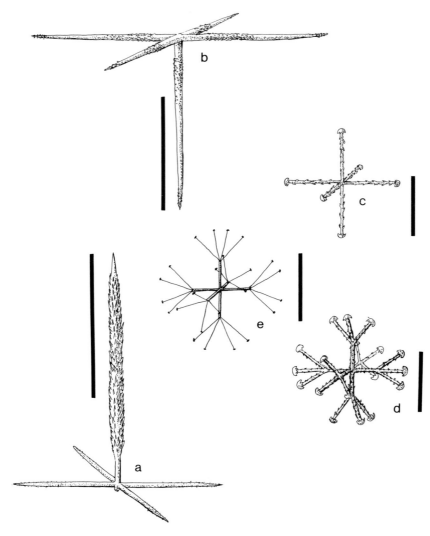

Fig. 28: *Caulophacus valdiviae.* a) dermal pentactine of inner (i.e. upper) dermal membrane, scale bar 200 μm; b) hypodermal pentactine, scale bar 500 μm; c) discohexactine; d) thick, spined discohexaster; scale bars c, d) 100 μm; e) thinrayed discohexaster, scale bar 50 μm. After Schulze (1904, plate 6).

83

Remarks: The species is known only from incomplete material, viz. a number of stalks. Spicules supposed to belong to the body were found loose in the cavity of some stalks, and allowed a partial reconstruction of the spicule complement and its characteristics.

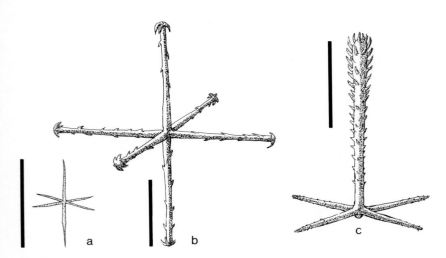

Fig. 29:   *Caulophacus antarcticus.* a) oxyhexactine, scale bar 100 μm; b) discohexactine, scale bar 50 μm; c) dermal pentactine of inner (i.e. upper) dermal membrane, scale bar 100 μm. After Schulze & Kirkpatrick (1910b, plate 1).

Caulophacus scotiae Topsent, 1910
Figure 30

Caulophacus scotiae Topsent, 1910: 10-12; 1913 (1920): 601-604, pl. 2, figs. 1-3, pl. 6, fig. 17; 1915b: 41-42.

Description: The sponge is up to at least 93 cm high, 85 cm of which is the stalk. The soft body is cupshaped, the wall becoming gradually thinner towards the rim, from 12 to 2 mm. The hollow stalk has a basal attachment plate and is 13 mm in diameter at the lower end, thickening to 37 mm at the upper end. The loose main skeleton comprises numerous diactines and rather few hexactines. The inner dermal hexactines with a much prolonged thin distal ray, the outer ones with a short, spiny distal ray. The inner and outer hypodermal pentactines are robust and alike each other; their unpaired ray is spiny and the paired rays are smooth. There are discohexactines, 180-220 μm in diameter, and 2 sizes of discohexasters, 70 - 80 μm and 330 μm in diameter, of which the first category is mostly found in the stalk.

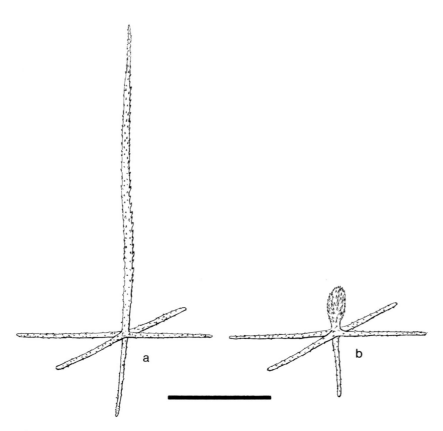

Fig. 30: *Caulophacus scotiae*. a) hexactine of inner (i.e. upper) dermal membrane; b) hexactine of outer (i.e. under) dermal membrane. Scale bar 250 μm. After Topsent (1913, plate 6).

Distribution: The single known specimen was taken at 2580 m depth in the eastern Weddell Sea.

Remarks: This is the largest known species of *Caulophacus*.

Caulophacus instabilis Topsent, 1910
Figure 31

Caulophacus instabilis Topsent, 1910: 12-15; 1913 (1920): 598-601, pl. 4, fig. 8, pl. 6, fig 16.

Description: Body form unknown. The hollow stalk is up to 9 mm in diameter, and probably up to at least 12 cm long. Outer dermal spicules are hexactines. Hypodermal spicules are pentactines with the unpaired ray clearly longer and more spiny than the paired rays. Main skeleton of diac-

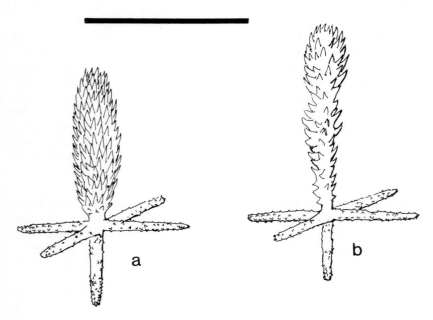

Fig. 31: *Caulophacus instabilis*. a) hexactine of outer (i.e. under) dermal membrane; b) hexactine from the stalk. Scale bar 200 μm. After Topsent (1913, plate 6).

tines and rather few hexactines. There are rare discohexactines, 155-190 µm in diameter, and commonly occurring discohexasters, 140 µm in diameter.

Distribution: The species is known from one specimen taken at 3248 m in the northern part of the Weddell Sea.

Remarks: Because of strong fragmentation, the species is very vaguely defined, the differences to other species being found only in the dimensions of spicules.

7.5.2.3 Family Rossellidae Schulze, 1886

Diagnosis: Body cup-, barrel- or sackshaped. Rooted by tufts of long basal pentactines, basal processes from the sponge body, or firmly attached at base. Large central cavity that opens through a large apical osculum. Outer dermal spicules rarely hexactines, normally spinulated pentactines which can be further reduced to tetractines or diactines. Outer hypodermal skeleton of either large pentactines or tangential bundles of diactines or both. The outer ends of the rather large hypodermal pentactines are sometimes lifted so that the paired rays form a veil-like structure at some distance from the surface of the sponge. Inner dermal spicules spinulated hexactines. Inner hypodermal skeleton a network of tangential bundles of diactines which are shorter than those of the main skeleton. No inner hypodermal pentactines. Main skeleton of long diactines, sometimes in combination with hexactines. Microscleres are different types of oxyhexasters and discohexasters, sometimes only one of these.

Remarks: The family Rossellidae comprises all the oftenmentioned large, mass-occurring hexactinellids from the Antarctic shelf. In a number of expeditions, members of this family were even the only hexactinellids collected (Kirkpatrick 1907; Topsent 1908, 1911, 1917; Burton 1929, 1932, 1934; Koltun 1976). From the early period of discovery up to about 1920, the number of genera, species and varieties of rossellids described from the Antarctic region rose steadily (Schulze 1886, 1887, 1904; Topsent 1902, 1913, 1917; Kirkpatrick 1907; Schulze & Kirkpatrick 1910). With increasing amounts of material at hand, some revisions became possible, and a series of synonymizations led to a drastic fall in the number of accepted species, and to doubt about the relevance of some genera (Burton 1929, Koltun 1976). We list species of five genera to have been recorded in Antarctica. A species of the genus *Staurocalyptus, S. roeperi* (Schulze, 1886) has been taken just outside the considered area.

KEY TO THE SPECIES OF ROSSELLIDAE KNOWN FROM THE ANTARCTIC REGION

1a	Microscleres comprise graphiocomes, but no oxyhexasters or small oxyhexactines 2
1b	Microscleres comprise oxyhexasters and /or small oxyhexactines, but not graphiocomes 3
2a(1a)	Inner and outer dermal spicules are spined hexactines with extremely short rays (Fig. 52a-b) ...... *Scolymastra joubini* p. 118
2b	Outer dermal spicules are tetractines, inner dermal spicules are hexactines, both with usual rays (Fig. 50b-c) ....*Anoxycalyx ijimai* p. 113
3a(1b)	Microscleres comprise oxyhexasters only .... *Bathydorus spinosus* p. 109
3b	Microscleres comprise oxyhexasters and/or small oxyhexactines and one to three other types of hexasters 4
4a(3b)	Microscleres are oxyhexasters and plumicomes .... *Calycosoma validum* p. 111
4b	Microscleres are oxyhexasters and/or small oxyhexactines, calycocomes and discohexasters 5
5a(4b)	Numerous hypodermal pentactines protrude from the surface . 6
5b	No (or only very few) hypodermal pentactines protrude from the surface 7
6a(5a)	Hypodermal pentactines rough with large scattered spines; basal pentactines anchorshaped with backwards pointing paired rays; calycocomes measuring up to about 100 μm in diameter ....*Rossella antarctica* p. 91
6b	Hypodermal pentactines more or less rough, without spines; basal pentactines with rays that are straight and at right angles to the shaft; calycocomes measure more than 150 μm, normally 300-480 μm in diameter .... *Rossella racovitzae* p. 93
7a(5b)	Small oxyhexactines present, no or few oxyhexasters 8
7b	Oxyhexasters present, no or few small oxyhexactines 9
8a(7a)	Small, 160-600 μm long, granulated, often wavy diactines present; surface without protruding spicule bundles; body soft, darkcoloured .... *Rossella fibulata* p. 97
8b	No small granulated diactines; surface with or without conules,

with numerous stout diactine bundles, up to 9 cm long; body
whitish stiff, incompressible .... *Rossella villosa* p. 95
9a(7b) Hypodermal skeleton of pentactines not present (diactines present) .... *Rossella vanhoeffeni* p. 104
9b   Hypodermal skeleton of pentactines (and diactines) present .. 10
10a(9b) Hypodermal pentactines found only in conules; calycocomes
130-230 µm in diameter; small discohexasters with secondary rays
of the same length .... *Rossella levis* p. 101
10b   Hypodermal pentactines found all over the surface, although
sometimes irregularly distributed; calycocomes 250 µm or more
in diameter; small discohexasters with secondary rays of two
lengths .... *Rossella nuda* p. 100

Genus ROSSELLA Carter, 1872

Diagnosis: Body sack-, cup- or barrelshaped with thick wall and large
inner cavity. Outer dermal spicules spinulated pentactines and some hexactines, rarely tetractines. Inner dermal spicules spinulated hexactines
and some pentactines. Hypodermal skeleton of pentactines strongly
developed in some species, reduced or absent in others; but then a more or
less strong hypodermal skeleton of diactines (which are different from
those of the main skeleton) is developed. Main skeleton of diactines and
sometimes scattered large hexactines. Microscleres are oxyhexasters,
calycocomes and two kinds of discohexasters.

Remarks: Ijima (1904) in one of the earliest surveys mentioned four
species of the genus *Rossella*. Some twenty years later, he (1927) could list
16 species and varieties, all except one from Antarctica, and a further 9
species and varieties in the very closely related genera *Gymnorossella* and
Aulorossella. Many of these taxa were nearly impossible to distinguish as
the descriptions were not easily comparable, scattered as they were in time
and appearing in different languages, and also different as to the degree
they gave details and in the spicule terminology used. To this came that
most species were based on a single or a few specimens, or even on
fragments only.

Although Topsent (1902) and Schulze & Kirkpatrick (1910 b) had pointed
to certain similarities among some taxa, Burton (1929) was the first to present a revised list of the Antarctic species of *Rossella* and related genera.
He synonymized *Aulorossella* with *Rossella* and recognized the five

species *Rossella antarctica, R. racovitzae, R. villosa, R. nuda* and *Gymnorossella inermis*, which by Koltun (1976) were reduced to two, *R. antarctica* and *R. racovitzae*. We agree to Koltun's synonymization of *Gymnorossella* with *Rossella*. At the species level we mostly follow Burton, because to encompass all the Antarctic *Rossella*s under two names leaves a situation with one well defined species and one which, also according to Koltun (1976), ".. is a highly polymorphic species".

The type species of *Rossella* is *R. antarctica*.

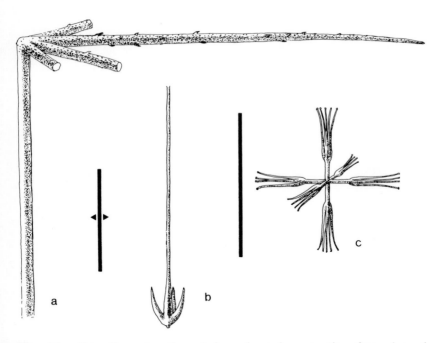

Fig. 32: *Rossella antarctica*. a) hypodermal pentactine from lateral spicule tuft; b) anchorshaped pentactine from the basal spicule tuft; scale bar 500 μm; c) calycocome, scale bar 100 μm. a, b) after Schulze (1887, plate 55), c) after Schulze & Kirkpatrick (1910b, plate 1).

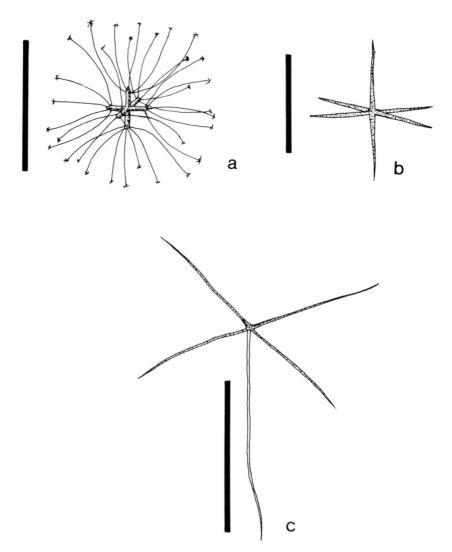

Fig. 33: *Rossella antarctica.* a) discohexaster, scale bar 40 μm; b) rough oxyhexactine, scale bar 100 μm; c) pentactine, scale bar 5 mm. After Schulze & Kirkpatrick (1910b, plate 1).

Rossella antarctica Carter, 1872
Figures 32, 33, 34

Rossella antarctica Carter, 1872: 414-417, pl. 21, figs. 1-10; 1875: 114-118, pl. 10, fig. 4.
Schulze 1887: 139-142, pl. 55, figs. 1-15. Schulze & Kirkpatrick 1910b: 15-17, pl. 1, figs. 2-2v.
Burton 1929: 405-407, fig. 1a. Koltun 1969: map 2; 1976: 165, pl.1, fig.1.
Rossella antarctica solida Kirkpatrick, 1907: 5-11, pl. 1, figs. 1-4, pl. 4, figs. 2-3.
Rossella antarctica gaussi Schulze & Kirkpatrick, 1910a: 296; 1910b pl. 2, figs. 1-1f.
Rossella antarctica intermedia Burton, 1932: 254-255, fig. 3b.
Acanthascus grossularia Schulze, 1886: 49; 1887: 145-147, pl. 56, figs. 1-12; 1897: 536-537.
? *Acanthascus dubius* Schulze, 1886: 49; 1887: 147-148, pl. 57, figs. 8-13.
Rhabdocalyptus australis Topsent, 1901: 6; 1902: 37-38, pl.2, figs. 5-6, pl. 4, figs. 14-21, pl. 5,
fig 1. Burton 1929: 407.

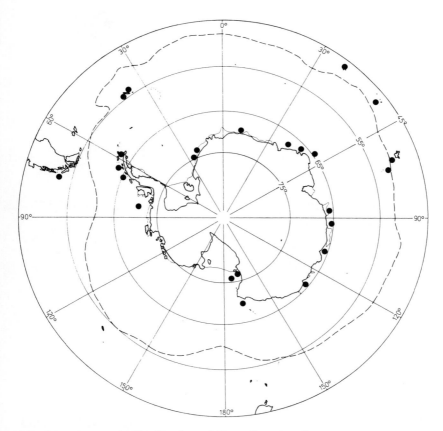

Fig. 34:   Antarctic distribution of *Rossella antarctica*.

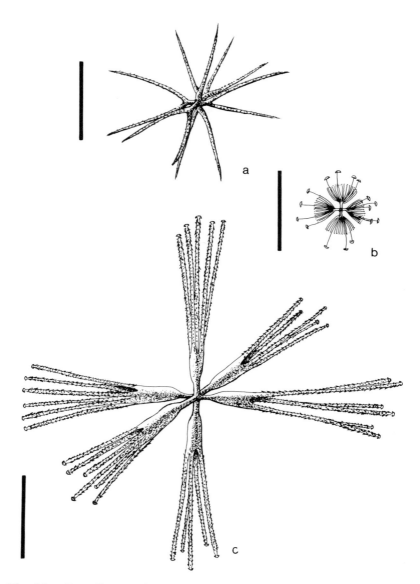

Fig. 35: *Rossella racovitzae.* a) oxyhexaster; b) discohexaster; only 4 of
the 6 rays depicted; c) calycocome. All scale bars 100 μm. Redrawn after
Topsent (1902, plate 4).

Diagnosis: Body spherical, barrel- or pearshaped with the upper end being the thickest, up to 30 cm high and 15 cm in diameter. Tissue firm, body rigid. Osculum large, circular, with a fringe of up to 1 cm long spicules at some distance from the edge. Outer surface with more or less pronounced, up to 4 mm high, regularly distributed conules, each bearing a spicule tuft. Some spicules in the tufts are diactines, others are pentactines, whose paired rays form a distinctive veil. The paired rays often point more or less to the same side of the smooth unpaired ray; they are rough and some of them have also conspicuous long scattered spines. Outer dermal spicules finely spinulated pentactines and some scattered hexactines. Inner dermal spicules finely spinulated hexactines. Main skeleton with rare hexactines. Base with a spicule tuft or fixed to hard substrate. The pentactines of the basal spicule tuft are pronouncedly anchorshaped. Microscleres: Oxyhexactines are about 140 μm in diameter and oxyhexasters about 120 μm. Calycocomes measure 70-100 μm in diameter and have 12-15 μm long primary rays, sometimes with a few small spines, a 2-4 μm long, poorly defined middlepiece, and 20-30 μm long faintly s-shaped nearly smooth secondary rays with small discs. Most discohexasters are 50-60 μm in diameter, and some rare ones are about 70 μm.

Distribution: *R. antarctica* is circumantarctic, at depths of 90-550 m. Outside the Antarctic it has been recorded from off Patagonia at 1100 m and off SW Africa at 200-300 m.

Rossella racovitzae Topsent, 1901
Figures 35, 36, plates III, IV

Rossella racovitzae Topsent, 1901: 5-6; 1902: 33-35, pl. 1, fig. 5, pl. 4, figs. 1-7; 1916: 3; 1917: 9-13, pl. 4, figs. 7-8 and 10, pl. 5, fig. 5. Kirkpatrick 1907: 14. Schulze & Kirkpatrick 1910a: 296-297; 1910b: 19-23, pl. 3, figs. 1-1m, 2. Burton 1929: 407-409, fig. 1, pl. 1 (further synonymy); 1932: 256-257; 1934: 7. Koltun 1969: map 2; 1976: 165 (pars).

Diagnosis: Body sackshaped, up to 20 cm high and 10 cm in diameter, with much variation in outer appearence. Sometimes occurring as groups, each consisting of numerous buds of different sizes still attached to stem specimens. Tissue firm, body rigid. Osculum without fringe of spicules, but long vertically oriented diactines are numerous in the upper part of the sponge. Outer surface mostly with flat conules with 10-15 mm long spicule tufts. Hypodermal pentactines are more or less protruding, their paired actines being at right angles to the unpaired ray, and usually forming a poorly defined veil. They are smooth except for the ray tips which are always coarsely granular, or they are granular in their full length. Outer dermal spicules are finely spinulated pentactines and hexactines mostly with rounded tips. Inner dermal spicules are finely spinulated hexactines with pointed actine ends. Main skeleton of diactines, many of which have rough rounded ends. The pentactines of the basal tuft have the 4-5 mm long paired rays at right angles to the unpaired ray. Microscleres: Oxyhexasters are 130-160 μm in diameter. Calycocomes measure 200-400 (490) μm in diameter and have short primary rays while

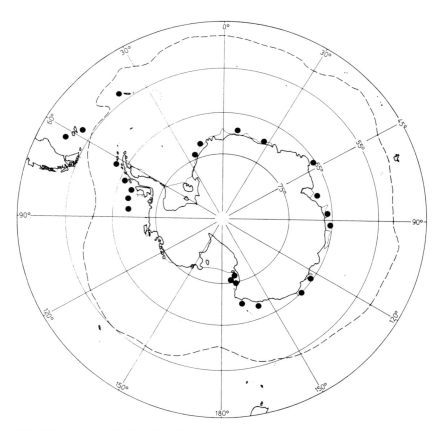

Fig. 36:   Antarctic distribution of *Rossella racovitzae*.

the middle piece is short or, most often, elongated; the 4-6 secondary rays are very long, covered with small recurved spines and have conspicuous dented discs. There are two kinds of discohexasters about 80 μm and 30-60 μm in diameter, respectively, the latter generally with secondary rays of two length categories.

Distribution: *R. racovitzae* is circumantarctic, at depths of 20-2000 m.

Remarks: Burton (1929) synonymized quite a number of species with *R. racovitzae*, and the synonymy list was further extended by Koltun (1976). On the basis of our own material (Collection from the EPOS III Expedition 1989, E. Weddell Sea) and literature studies, we for the time being reestablish *Rossella villosa* Burton, 1929, *R. fibulata* Schulze & Kirkpatrick, 1910, *R. nuda* Topsent, 1901, *R. levis* (Kirkpatrick, 1910) and *R. vanhoeffeni* (Schulze & Kirkpatrick, 1910). At present we cannot go further, but it should be emphasized that in the concept of *R. racovitzae* as given above the species is still polymorphic, and with time it may be further split; one candidate for an independant taxon is the strongly bud-producing type briefly characterized.

<u>*Rossella villosa*</u> Burton, 1929
Figure 37, plate V

Rossella villosa Burton, 1929: 412-413, pl. 3; 1932: 257. Koltun 1969: map 2; 1976: 165.

Diagnosis: Body sackshaped, more or less spherical, up to 30 cm high and 16 cm in diameter. Tissue firm, body rigid. Osculum up to 8 cm in diameter, with a fringe of spicules at some distance from the rim. Outer surface even or with flat conules, and with regularly scattered tufts of about 15 stout diactines which are up to 13 cm long (9 cm free), sometimes intermingled with single pentactines. Hypodermal pentactines in or just beneath the outer surface. Basal spicule tuft composed of up to 18 cm long and 300-400 μm thick pentactines with straight 1-2 mm long paired rays at right angles to the unpaired ray and often turned to the same side. Microscleres: There are numerous oxyhexactines 100-150 μm in diameter. Oxyhexasters, 110-150 μm in diameter, are rare. Calycocomes measure 185-260 μm in diameter, have a very short middlepiece and 4-6 finely granulated secondary rays with distinct discs. Discohexactines are 100-300 μm in diameter. Discohexasters are about 40 μm in diameter and have secondary rays of two lengths.

Distribution: Off Palmer Archipelago, in the Eastern Weddell Sea, off Oates Land and off Victoria Land, at depths of 90-370 m (Fig. 37).

Remarks: The original description by Burton is without many details and especially short regarding the spicules, which were just said to be as in *R. nuda*. Koltun (1976) somewhat hesitatingly synonymized the species with *R. racovitzae* as forma *villosa*. In the description we have added the most necessary measurements of microscleres from our own specimens from the eastern Weddell Sea.

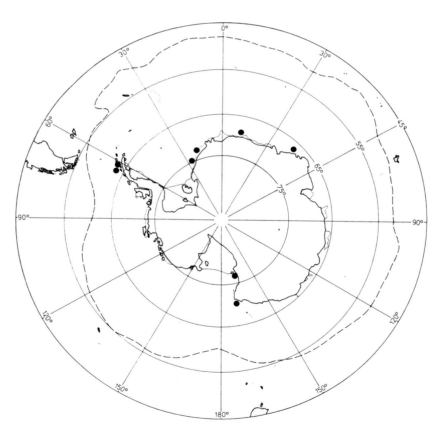

Fig. 37: Antarctic distribution of Rossella villosa.

Rossella fibulata Schulze & Kirkpatrick, 1910
Figure 38, plates VI, VII, VIII

Rossella fibulata Schulze & Kirkpatrick 1910a: 298-299; 1910b: 27-29, pl. 7, figs. 2-2n.

Diagnosis: Body barrel- to broad vaseshaped, up to about 80 cm high and 70 cm in diameter. Bodywall up to 8 cm thick at base. Oscule up to 50 cm in diameter, with very thin rim and a low fringe of spicules. Colour, both alive and in alcohol, dark brown to reddish brown, sometimes pink. Soft and easily damaged, especially the larger specimens, which collapse in air. Specimens less than about 20 cm in height smooth or with only few small conules, while larger specimens have numerous conspicuous conules without spicule tufts. The largest conules are up to 6 cm in height and diameter, are somewhat flattened and easily torn off. They are mostly found on the lower two thirds of the body, the upper part being smooth. The excurrent canals open directly into the central cavity, without being covered by a spicule latticework. Outer dermal spicules are coarsely spinulated pentactines and some hexactines. No or few hypodermal pentactines. Somewhat irregular hypodermal network of strong diactine bundles. Inner dermal spicules coarsely spinulated hexactines and pentactines. Main skeleton of diactines and some hexactines with spinulated actine tips. Short basal tuft of pentactines with the paired rays at right angles to the unpaired ray, and usually all turned to the same side. Microscleres: Hexasters are rather few, measuring about 80 μm in diameter, small hexactines, 100-120 μm in diameter, being much more common together with tetractines, triactines, diactines and intergrading forms between these categories; they have mostly prolonged rays and are all finely granulated. These microsclere diactines are very numerous, can be up to 600 μm long, and some of them have taken very peculiar bent and folded forms. Calycocomes measure 164-350 μm in diameter, have primary rays of about 16 μm length, strong middle piece 10-25 μm long, and 4-7 stout, finely granulated secondary rays rounded in the outer end. There seems to be only one kind of discohexaster, 40 μm in diameter, with secondary rays of two lengths.

Distribution: The species is known from localities in the eastern Weddell Sea and off Wilhelm II Land, at depths from 180-460 m.

Remarks: When describing *R. fibulata*, Schulze & Kirkpatrick (1910a, b) had only 3 small fragments, which did not allow them to give more than a description of the spicules. Burton (1929) synonymized the species with

R. racovitzae, being of the opinion that the many strange derivations of the hexasters were abnormalities of no importance. We have found these modifications to be very numerous and constantly occurring in our material, and this, taken together with the well defined gross morphology, define the species very clearly. Some of the spicule measuremens given come from our material.

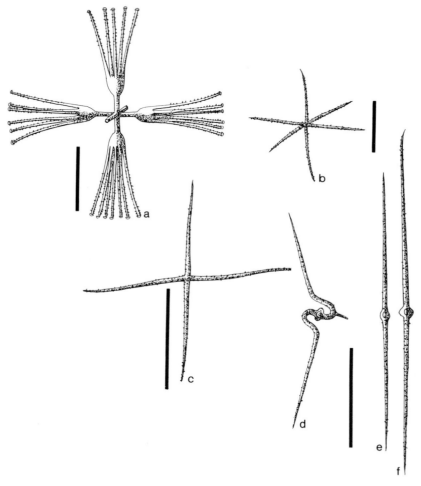

Fig. 38: *Rossella fibulata.* a) calycocome; b) hexactine; scale bars a, b) 50 μm; c) stauractine; d-f) diactines; scale bars c-f) 100 μm. After Schulze & Kirkpatrick (1910 b, plate 7).

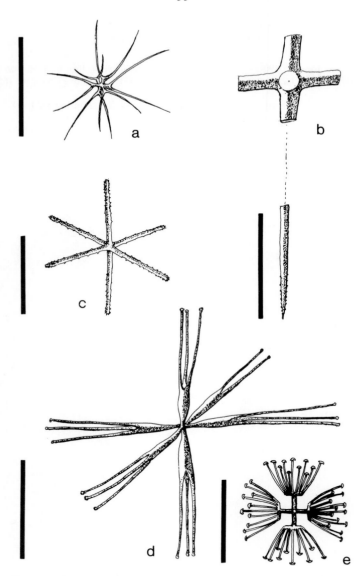

Fig. 39: *Rossella nuda*. a) oxyhexaster; b) part of hypodermal pentactine; scale bars a, b) 100 μm; c) inner dermal hexactine, scale bar 200 μm;
d) calycocome, scale bar 100 μm; e) discohexaster, scale bar 30 μm. a-d)
after Topsent (1902, plate 4), e) after Kirkpatrick (1907, plate 4).

Rossella nuda Topsent, 1901
Figures 39, 40, plates IX, X

Rossella nuda Topsent, 1901: 4-5; 1902: 32-33, pl. 1, fig. 7, pl. 4, figs. 8-13. Burton 1929 (pars): 409-412, figs. 1-2, pl. 2 ; 1932: 255-256, figs. 1-2; 1934: 7. Koltun 1976 (pars): 165, pl. 1, pl. 2, pl. 3.
Hyalascus hodgsoni Kirkpatrick, 1907: 3-5, pl.3, fig. 1, pl. 4, fig. 1. Burton 1929: 411.

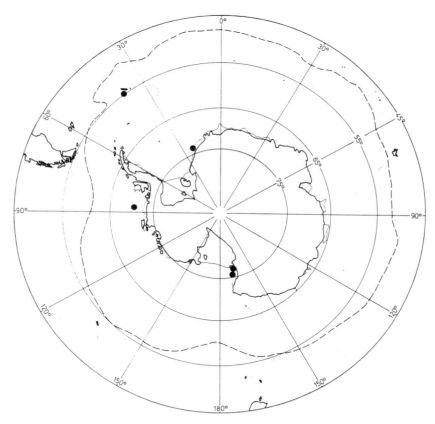

Fig. 40: Distribution of *Rossella nuda*. Because of synonymizations it is not possible to distinguish the *R. nuda* in Burton (1929) and Koltun (1976) from their *R. racovitzae*.

Diagnosis: Body sackshaped, more or less cylindrical, up to 75 cm high and 30 cm in diameter. Soft tissue, body collapses in air. Colour fresh and in alcohol pale brownish-yellow or greyish. No fringe of spicules near the osculum. Outer surface even or with some conules, which may bear spicule tufts consisting of long diactines. Outer dermal spicules spinulated pentactines and hexactines, sometimes also tetractines. Hypodermal pentactines smooth with spined tips, at level with surface, are found scattered. Hypodermal diactines, 2500-3500 μm, form an open tangential network. Inner dermal spicules spinulated hexactines. Main skeleton of diactines only, with smooth or faintly rough pointed ends. Basal tuft varies in size. The anchoring pentactines seem to have the paired rays at right angles to the unpaired, although sometimes somewhat backwards curved. Microscleres: Oxyhexasters measure about 120 μm in diameter. Calycocomes measure 250 μm or more in diameter and have 15 μm long primary rays, a 25 μm long middle piece, and 2-4 very long, thin, smooth or finely granulated secondary rays with small discs. Two kinds of discohexasters measure up to 100 μm and 40-75 μm in diameter, respectively; the smaller category has secondary rays of two lengths.

Distribution: The species is known from localities in the Bellingshausen Sea, off South Georgia and along the coast from the eastern Weddell Sea to the Ross Sea off Victoria Land, at depths from 35-900 m.

Rossella levis (Kirkpatrick, 1907)
Figures 41, 42, plates XI, XII

Aulorossella levis Kirkpatrick, 1907: 17-19, pl. 2, figs. 2-3, pl. 6, fig. 3.
Aulorossella pilosa Kirkpatrick, 1907: 16-17, pl. 2, fig. 1, pl. 6, fig. 2. Topsent 1917: 17-18.
Aulorossella longstaffi Kirkpatrick, 1907: 19-20, pl. 2, fig. 4, pl. 7, fig. 1.
Aulorossella gaini Topsent, 1916: 164-165; 1917: 18-19, pl. 5, fig. 2.
Anaulosoma schulzei Kirkpatrick, 1907: 21-23, pl. 3, figs. 5-6, pl. 5, fig. 2. Burton 1929: 411.

Diagnosis: Body sackshaped, up to 30 cm (possibly 60 cm) high and 33 cm (possibly 45 cm) in diameter. Body wall up to at least 3 cm thick. Colour in life pale yellow; in alcohol varying from pale yellow to dark brown. Oscule contracts strongly during preservation. Outer surface with conspicuous conules, mostly with tufts of diactines that can be at least 3 cm long. Outer dermal spicules coarsely spinulated pentactines. Hypodermal pentactines rather few with short paired rays (< about 600 μm), occurring only in the surface of the conules, sometimes projecting into the spicule

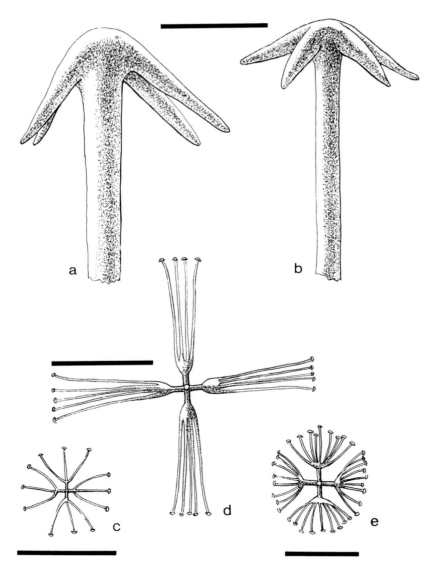

Fig. 41: *Rossella levis*. a) basal pentactine; b) hypodermal pentactine; scale bar 500 μm; c) discohexaster, scale bar 100 μm; d) calycocome, scale bar 100 μm; e) discohexaster, scale bar 25 μm. c-e) only four rays depicted. After Kirkpatrick (1907, plate 6).

tufts. Hypodermal diactines form a well developed tangential network. Inner dermal spicules mostly coarsely spinulated pentactines with some hexactines. Main skeleton of diactines and hexactines, the latter sometimes with four rays curved parallelly to one of the other rays. Basal tuft of anchorshaped pentactines. Microscleres: Small oxyhexactines (normal oxyhexasters are uncommon) 55-180 μm in diameter. Calycocomes 130-230 μm in diameter, with primary rays 8-12 μm long, a middle piece 6-12 μm long, and 4-8 slender, sometimes granulated secondary rays with small discs. Two types of discohexasters (can be rare) measuring 45-97 μm

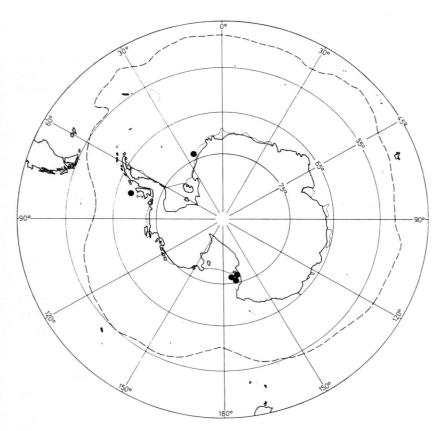

Fig. 42:   Antarctic distribution of *Rossella levis*.

and 34-47 μm in diameter, respectively; in the smaller category the secondary rays all have the same length.

Distribution: *R. levis* has been found at a number of localities in the Bellingshausen Sea, the eastern Weddell Sea and off Victoria Land, at depths of 18-385 m. It may have been taken at more localities off the coast from Enderby Land to Adélie Land, but referred to as *R. racovitzae* by Koltun (1976).

Remarks: Because a good deal of overlap is found in the variation of the morphological characters between *R. levis* and *R. vanhoeffeni*, it is worth to point out a number of additional characters for distinction between the two, other than those used in the key. In *R. levis* the calycocomes measure less than 230 μm and the larger discohexasters, which are often rare, less than 95 μm in diameter. The small discohexasters generally have secondary rays all of the same length or only somewhat unequal. In *R. vanhoeffeni* the calycocomes sometimes measure more than 230 μm, while the larger discohexasters are more than 90 μm in diameter. The small discohexasters have secondary rays of two well distinguished lengths.

Rossella vanhoeffeni (Schulze & Kirkpatrick, 1910)
Figures 43, 44, plates XIII, XIV, XV

Aulorossella vanhoeffeni Schulze & Kirkpatrick, 1910a: 300-301; 1910b: 33-36, pl. 5, figs. 1-1y, pl. 6, figs. 1-1d.
Aulorossella vanhoeffeni armata Schulze & Kirkpatrick, 1910a: 301; 1910b: 36-38, pl. 6, figs. 2-5. Burton 1929: 411.
Aulorossella aperta Topsent, 1916: 165; 1917: 20-22, pl. 4, fig. 4, pl. 5, fig. 3.
Gymnorossella inermis Topsent, 1916: 164; 1917: 22-26, pl. 1, fig. 1, pl. 5, fig. 4. Burton 1929: 413; 1932: 257, fig. 3.

Diagnosis: Body barrel- or sackshaped, up to 30 cm high and 26 cm in diameter. Body wall up to 2 cm thick. Colour alive pale yellow or yellowish grey, in alcohol yellowish grey. Oscule up to at least 17 cm in diameter, contracts during preservation. Outer surface smooth or with low conules bearing tufts of diactines. Outer dermal spicules are coarsely spinulated pentactines and hexactines. No or very few hypodermal pentactines. Hypodermal network of diactines well developed. Inner dermal spicules are coarsely spinulated hexactines. Main skeleton consists of thin smooth often curved diactines and few hexactines with rays that are smooth except at the tips. Basal tuft of anchorshaped pentactines.

Microscleres: Oxyhexasters measuring 95-140 μm in diameter. Calycocomes 140-380 μm in diameter, the primary rays being about 14 μm long, the
middle piece shorter than that and sometimes only indicated, and the 2-7
granulated secondary rays are somewhat s-shaped with small discs. Two
types of discohexasters measuring 90-160 μm (can be rare) and 40-85 μm
in diameter, respectively; the smaller category has secondary rays of two
clearly different lengths.

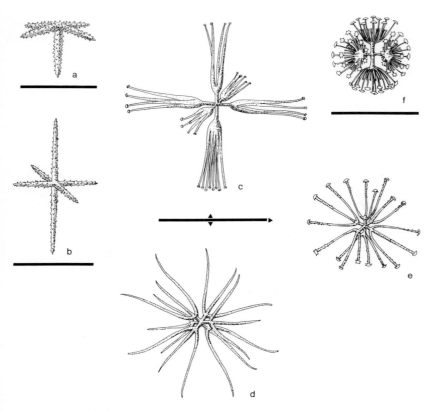

Fig. 43:   *Rossella vanhoeffeni*. a) pentactine of the outer dermal layer; b)
hexactine of the inner dermal layer; scale bars a-b) 200 μm; c) calycocome;
d) oxyhexaster; e) discohexaster; scale bar c-e) 100 μm; f) small discohexaster with rays of two different lengths, only 4 rays depicted, scale bar 50
μm. After Schulze & Kirkpatrick (1910b, plate 5).

Distribution: *R. vanhoeffeni* has been recorded from localities in the Bellingshausen Sea, off the Palmer Archipelago, off the Falkland Islands, the eastern Weddell Sea and off Wilhelm II Land, at depths of 50-460 m. It may have been taken on more localities off the coast from Enderby Land to Adélie Land, but referred to as *R. racovitzae* by Koltun (1976).

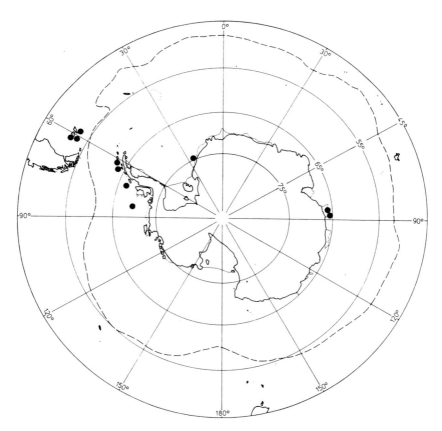

Fig. 44: Antarctic distribution of *Rossella vanhoeffeni*.

Remarks: The specimens described by Schulze & Kirkpatrick (1910b) as *R. vanhoeffeni armata* have few scattered hypodermal pentactines, which are distributed with the largest number at the base and fewer towards the oscular end. All the specimens were small and it is possible that the pentactines in this species are found in young specimens and lost with age.

Genus BATHYDORUS Schulze, 1886

Diagnosis: Body sack- or chaliceshaped, calyculate or lamellar, with thin (1-2.5 mm), loose wall. The oscular margin is fringed with projecting spicules, and can be bent outwards to form a horizontal rim 15-20 mm broad. Outer dermal spicules mainly spiny tetractines, but other numbers of rays often occur. Inner dermal spicules spiny hexactines. Main skeleton of diactines. Microscleres oxyhexasters only.

Remarks: The genus comprises 9 nominal species and a number of varieties, mostly reported from bathyal and abyssal depths, and often only once. Many of these are very much alike (Schulze 1895) and may be

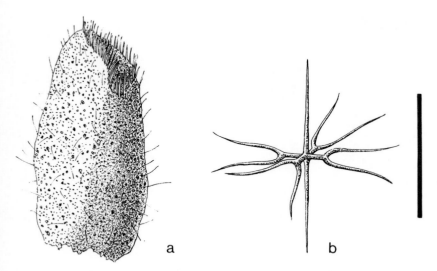

a   b

Fig. 45: *Bathydorus spinosus*. a) habitus, about original size; b) oxyhexaster, scale bar 100 μm. After Schulze (1887, plate 59)

108

conspecific (Koltun 1976). One species has been reported from Antarctica, and one, *B. stellatus* Schulze, 1886, has been taken just outside the considered area.

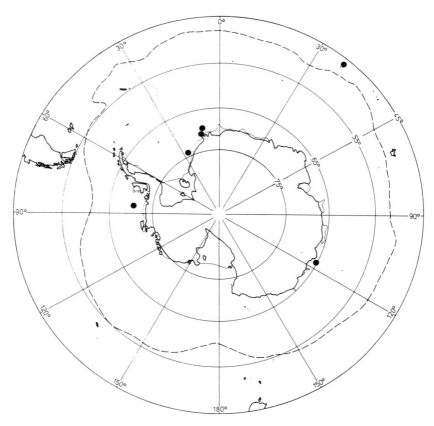

Fig. 46: Antarctic distribution of *Bathydorus spinosus*.

Bathydorus spinosus Schulze, 1886.
Figures 45, 46, plates XVI, XVII, XVIII

Bathydorus spinosus Schulze 1887: 153-154, pl. 59, figs. 6-9. Topsent 1901: 6; 1902: 36, pl. 1, fig. 1. Koltun 1976: 165.
Bathydorus levis var. *ciliatus* Topsent, 1910: 15-16; 1913 (1920): 604-605, pl. 1, figs. 6-7.

Diagnosis: Sack- or chaliceshaped with thin wall, up to 20 cm high and 13 cm in diameter. Osculum with spicule fringe. The outside is more or less spiny from protruding diactines, reaching up to 6 mm above the surface. In large specimens there are scattered small conules. The inner dermal hexactines measure 135-300 µm largest dimension. Microscleres are oxyhexasters, 90-150 µm in diameter.

Distribution: *B. spinosus* is known from five localities in the Bellingshausen Sea, the eastern Weddell Sea, and near Crozet Islands (Penguin Island), at depths from 569 - 4847 m.

Remarks: *Bathydorus spinosus* and *B. levis* are here considered synonymous following indications of various authors (Schulze 1897, Lendenfeld 1915, Koltun 1976). When the descriptions of the two species and their varieties are taken together, not a single character seems to be usable for distinction.

Genus CALYCOSOMA Schulze, 1899

Diagnosis: Body funnelshaped, on the outside with scattered conules bearing thin spicule tufts, on the inner side smooth. Body wall pronouncedly thicker and firmer in lower part than in upper. Outer dermal spicules spined hexactines and some pentactines, inner dermal spicules spined hexactines. Hypodermal pentactines under the conules have the paired rays bent backwards in the middle in a sharp angle creating a fishhook-like structure. Main skeleton of bundles of large diactines and scattered hexactines. Microscleres are oxyhexasters and plumicomes.

Remarks: The modification of the hypodermal pentactines under the conules is described from the Antarctic material (Topsent 1913); it is not clear whether it is also found in the type material. The genus comprises only one species.

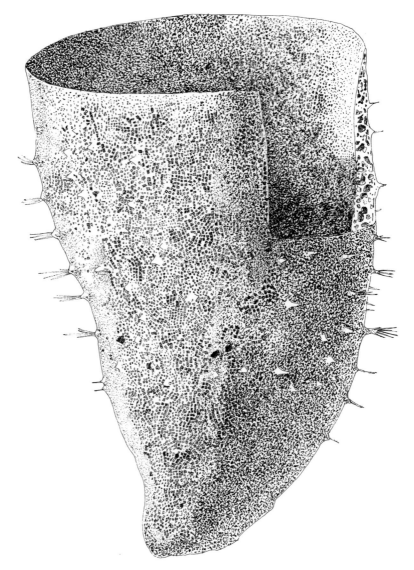

Fig. 47: *Calycosoma validum*. Habitus, about original size. After Schulze (1899, plate 4).

111

Calycosoma validum Schulze, 1899
Figures 47, 48, 49

Calycosoma validum Topsent, 1910: 17-18; 1913 (1920): 606-607, pl. 3, fig. 2, pl. 6, fig. 5.

Diagnosis: As for the genus. The funnelshaped body is up to 14 cm high and 8 cm in diameter at the upper end. The body wall has a thickness of 10 mm in the lower part, and gradually becomes thinner towards the upper rim. The conules are about 4 mm high and 1-2 mm in diameter, and the spicule tufts are 5-15 mm long. Inner and outer dermal hexactines are different in size and spinulation. The oxyhexasters measure about 100-180 μm in diameter. The plumicomes measure 36-70 μm in diameter.

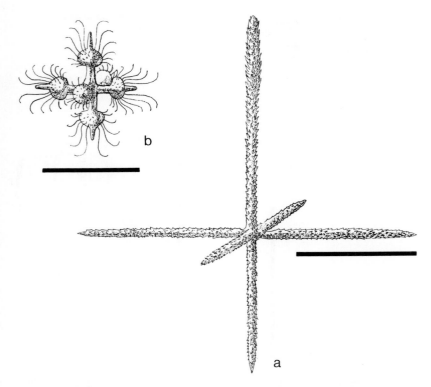

Fig. 48: *Calycosoma validum*. a) hexactine of outer dermal layer, scale bar 100 μm; b) plumicome, scale bar 20 μm. After Schulze (1899, plate 4).

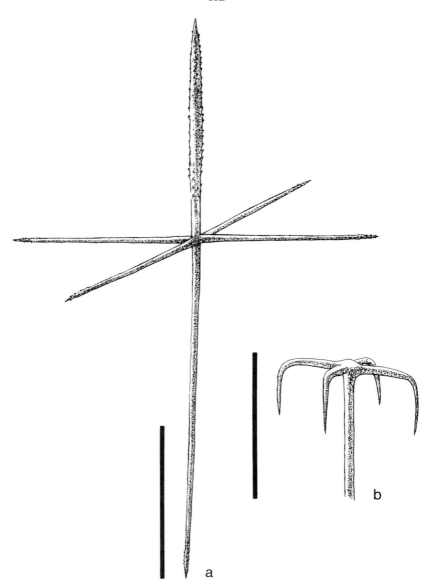

Fig. 49: *Calycosoma validum.* a) very large hexactine of inner dermal layer, scale bar 400 μm; b) pentactine, scale bar 400 μm. After Topsent (1913, plate 6).

113

Distribution: The single Antarctic record is from 3266 m near the South Orkney Islands. Outside Antarctica *C. validum* is known from one locality at abyssal depths of the North Atlantic.

Remarks: The two known specimens were damaged at the upper edge, and it is not known whether there is a fringe of spicules at the oscular margin. Topsent (1913) pointed out some differences in spicule dimensions between the Atlantic and the Antarctic specimens, but he did not consider these important enough to serve for a distinction of a separate Antarctic species. The oxyhexasters measured 150-180 μm in diameter, and the plumicomes 60-70 μm.

Genus ANOXYCALYX Kirkpatrick, 1907

Diagnosis: Body sackshaped, somewhat compressed. Outer surface with conules, with scattered spicule tufts. Osculum terminal, without fringe of spicules. The outer dermal spicules tetractines, the inner hexactines, both finely spined. The hypodermal spicules are smooth pentactines with strongly curved paired rays; they are confined to the conules. The main skeleton is formed of bundles of diactines. Microscleres are two types of discohexasters and graphiocomes.

Remarks: The genus contains two species of which one is found in Antarctica.

Anoxycalyx ijimai Kirkpatrick, 1907
Figures 50, 51

Anoxycalyx ijimai Kirkpatrick, 1907: 23-24, pl. 3, fig. 7, pl. 7, fig. 2. Schulze & Kirkpatrick 1910a: 301-302; 1910b: 44-48, pl. 7, figs. 1-1m. Topsent 1917: 26. Burton 1929: 413; 1934: 8. Koltun 1976: 166.

Diagnosis: Body up to 7 cm high and 3 cm in diameter. Body wall firm and up to 8 mm thick. The oval, rather narrow osculum measures about 10 mm maximum dimension. The outer surface with small conules and up to 5 cm long tufts of spicules. Discohexasters of a special type, which have the secondary rays arranged in several whorls, measure 175-255 μm in diameter, while normal discohexasters are 40-120 μm, and graphiocomes with very diverging secondary rays 120-220 μm in diameter. Often with numerous buds, 2-6 mm in diameter.

114

Fig. 50: *Anoxycalyx ijimai.* a) hypodermal pentactine, scale bar 1 mm; b) tetractine of outer dermal layer, scale bar 200 μm; c) hexactine of inner dermal layer, scale bar 100 μm; d) graphiocome; e) discohexaster; scale bar d, e) 100 μm; d, e) only 4 rays depicted. After Kirkpatrick (1907, plate 7).

Distribution: *A. ijimai* is circumantarctic, at depths from 46-603 m.

Genus SCOLYMASTRA Topsent, 1910

Diagnosis: Body sackshaped with very large inner cavity. Outer and inner surfaces smooth. Basal part with long anchoring spicules. Outer and inner dermal spicules are spiny hexactines with thick, very short rays. Each layer of hexactines is supported by a network of tangentially oriented diactines. Beneath the outer dermal layer, there are hypodermal

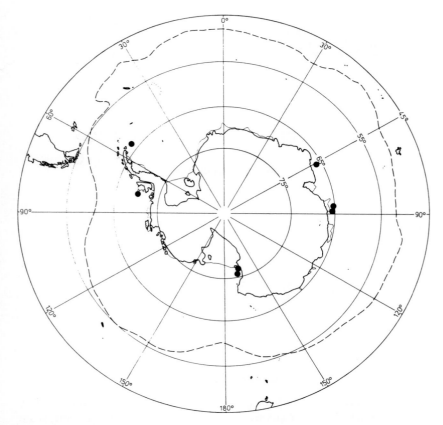

Fig. 51: Antarctic distribution of *Anoxycalyx ijimai*.

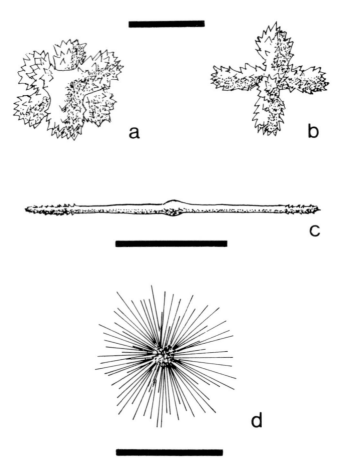

Fig. 52: *Scolymastra joubini.* a) dermal hexactine; b) dermal hexactine, scale bar a, b) 50 μm; c) diactine, scale bar 200 μm; d) graphiocome, scale bar 200 μm. After Topsent (1917, plate 5).

pentactines. Main skeleton of long diactines and strong hexactines, both with spined ray tips. Microscleres are two types of discohexasters and graphiocomes.

Remarks: The genus contains one species.

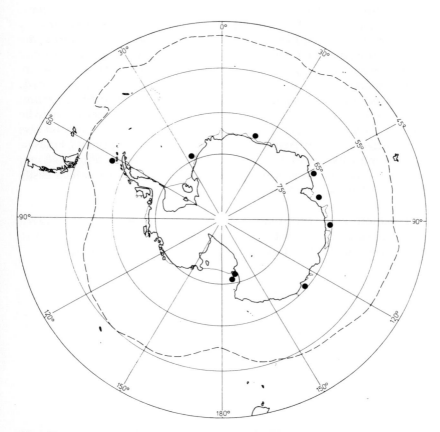

Fig. 53:   Antarctic distribution of *Scolymastra joubini*.

Scolymastra joubini Topsent, 1910
Figures 52, 53, plates XIX, XX, XXI

Scolymastra joubini Topsent, 1916: 163; 1917: 27-31, pl. 2, fig. 4, pl. 5, fig. 1. Burton 1929: 413-414. Dayton et. al. 1974: 107, fig. 2. Dayton 1979: 272, fig. 1. Koltun 1969: map 2.

Diagnosis: Body up to 2 m high and about 70 cm in diameter, but generally much smaller and then often pearshaped, being thickest in the lower part. Body wall firm, rather incompressible, in specimens about 50 cm tall up to about 7 cm thick in the basal part. Oscule large, can contract when preserved; with fringe of scattered stout long diactines and some pentactines resembling those in the basal tuft. With short broad basal spicule tuft of pentactines with paired rays at right angles to the shaft. Colour alive a pale yellow. The compact dermal hexactines measure only 65-90 μm in diameter. Larger spined hexactines, 140 μm in diameter, are found scattered among the much more numerous small ones in the inner dermal layer. The tangential layers of diactines, 360 - 2000 μm long, are well developed. The hypodermal pentactines have a very long inwards directed ray, while the paired rays vary much in length, from 550-2200 μm; they are smooth except at the tips. The hypodermal pentactines seem to be absent in some specimens. Discohexasters with long, thin, wavy end rays which originate at different levels from the end of the primary hexaster ray, are up to 400 μm in diameter; normal discohexasters about 140 μm; numerous graphiocomes with strongly diverging end rays, which easily break off, 220-240 μm in diameter.

Distribution: Recorded from the South Shetland Islands, in the eastern Weddell Sea and in a number of places along the Antarctic east coast to McMurdo Sound off Victoria Land, at depths of about 50-440 m.

8. DISTRIBUTION

The distribution patterns of species around the Antarctic continent can be related to the topography of the shelf and slope and to the hydrography. The shelf is rather narrow exept for some areas in the Bellingshausen Sea, the Weddell Sea and the Ross Sea, and the break to the slope lies generally rather deep, between 500 and 800 m. Compared to other parts of the world, the hydrographic conditions are rather uniform from the surface to the upper slope.

By far the largest number of samples of Antarctic hexactinellids comes from the shelf. There are only two records from the slope (800-2000 m), and 17 from depths around 2000 m and downwards.

The Antarctic hexactinellid fauna comprises 28 species as treated here, and a further 10 may be considered in the distribution analysis because they have been recorded close to the Antarctic convergence, mainly in deep water (*Hyalonema clavigerum* Schulze, 1886, *H. conus* Schulze, 1886, *Holascus fibulatus* Schulze, 1886, *H. polajevi* Schulze, 1886, *Malacosaccus vastus* Schulze, 1886, *Sympagella johnstoni* (Schulze, 1886), *Caulophacus latus* Schulze, 1886, *C. pipetta* (Schulze, 1886), *Staurocalyptus roeperi* (Schulze, 1886), *Bathydorus stellatus* Schulze, 1886. There is a distinct vertical division into a shelf group of species and a deep-water group. The relatively few species on the shelf are present in high numbers and give rise to large biomasses. By species number, however, hexactinellids are a predominantly deep-sea group in Antarctica, as they are in other oceans.

From the shelf area 14 species have been recorded, 10 of which belong to the same family, the Rossellidae. Of the 14 species, 9 have only been recorded in shelf depths, and one mainly on the shelf, rarely on the slope. Of the remaining 5, 3 are perhaps also restricted to the shelf, since the deeper records comprise dead skeleton fragments that can have been washed down along the slope; the last two are deep-sea species extending their ranges upwards, both in the Bellingshausen Sea. The 8 most commonly recorded shelf species are all circumantarctic in distribution, with depth ranges from about 50 - 600 m. The other 6 are known from very few records. Two of these species have been taken only on the shelf, the others both in Antarctic shelf areas and at abyssal depths in the southernmost parts of the Atlantic and Indian Oceans, for which reason they may be presumed also to occur on the Antarctic slope.

The two known records from the slope are rare occurrences of species elsewise found on the shelf, but it should be emphasized that the slope is a largely uninvestigated environment.

In Antarctic abyssal depths 23 species have been recorded, but only 5 of these are common with other oceans. The high number found so far only in the Antarctic deep-sea is, however, probably not an example of "high endemism" but rather reflects the poor knowledge of deep-sea faunas in general, and to a certain degree presumably also the lack of revisions of the group. Most species belong to genera well known from other deep-sea areas. Little can be said about geographical distribution as 16 species are known from only one record, 5 have been taken 2-3 times, and only 2 five times or more.

121

9. SYNONYMY LIST

The names listed on the left side are those used in the previous Antarctic literature; those to the right are the synonyms as used in this volume. Details can be found in Schulze & Kirkpatrick (1910b), Ijima (1927), Burton (1929), Reiswig (1990), and here.

Acanthascus dubius Schulze, 1886 = ? *Rossella antarctica* Carter, 1872.
Acanthascus grossularia Schulze, 1886 = *Rossella antarctica* Carter, 1872.
Anaulosoma schulzei Kirkpatrick, 1907 = *Aulorossella levis* Kirkpatrick, 1907.
Aulorossella aperta Topsent, 1916 = *A. vanhoeffeni* Schulze & Kirkpatrick, 1910.
A. gaini Topsent 1916 = *A. levis* Kirkpatrick, 1907.
A. longstaffi Kirkpatrick, 1907 = *A. levis* Kirkpatrick, 1907.
A. pilosa Kirkpatrick, 1907 = *A. levis* Kirkpatrik, 1907.
A. vanhoeffeni vanhoeffeni Schulze & Kirkpatrick, 1910 = *A. vanhoeffeni* Schulze & Kirkpatrick, 1910.
A. vanhoeffeni armata Schulze & Kirkpatrick, 1910 = *A. vanhoeffeni* Schulze & Kirkpatrick, 1910.
Bathydorus levis Schulze, 1895 = *B. spinosus* Schulze, 1886.
B. levis ciliatus Topsent, 1910 = *B. spinosus* Schulze, 1886.
Chonelasma lamella choanoides Schulze & Kirkpatrick, 1910 = *C. lamella* Schulze, 1886.
Gymnorossella inermis Topsent, 1916 = *Aulorossella vanhoeffeni* Schulze & Kirkpatrick, 1910.
Hyalascus hodgsoni Kirkpatrick, 1907 = *Rossella nuda* Topsent, 1901.
Rhabdocalyptus australis Topsent, 1901 = *Rossella antarctica* Carter, 1872.
Rossella antarctica antarctica Carter, 1872 = *R. antarctica* Carter, 1872.
R. antarctica gaussi Schulze & Kirkpatrick 1910 = *R. antarctica* Carter, 1872.
R. antarctica intermedia Burton, 1932 = *R. antarctica* Carter, 1872.
R. antarctica solida Kirkpatrick, 1907 = *R. antarctica* Carter, 1872.
R. dubia (Schulze, 1886) = ?*R. antarctica* Carter, 1872.
R. gaussi Schulze & Kirkpatrick, 1910 = *R. racovitzae* Topsent, 1901.
R. hexactinophila Kirkpatrick, 1907 = *R. racovitzae* Topsent, 1901.
R. lychnophora Schulze & Kirkpatrick, 1910 = *R. racovitzae* Topsent, 1901.

R. mixta Schulze & Kirkpatrick, 1910 = *R. racovitzae* Topsent, 1901.

R. podagrosa Kirkpatrick, 1907 = *R. racovitzae* Topsent, 1901.

R. podagrosa tenuis Topsent, 1917 = *R. racovitzae* Topsent, 1901.

R. racovitzae hexactinophila Schulze & Kirkpatrick, 1910 = *R. racovitzae* Topsent, 1901.

R. racovitzae microdiscina Topsent, 1917 = *R. racovitzae* Topsent, 1901.

R. racovitzae minuta Schulze & Kirkpatrick, 1910 = *R. racovitzae* Topsent, 1901.

R. racovitzae racovitzae Topsent, 1901 = *R. racovitzae* Topsent, 1901.

Unicinatera plicata Topsent, 1901 = *Chonelasma lamella* Schulze, 1886.

10. References

Afzelius, B. A. (1961a) Some problems of ciliary structure and ciliary function. In: Goodwin T. W. & O. Lindberg (eds.) Biological structure and function, Proc. first IUB/IUBS Int. Symp. Stockholm, **2**: 558-567
--- (1961b) Flimmer-flagellum of the sponge. Nature **191**: 1318-1319
Barthel, D. (1992 a) Antarctic hexactinellids: A taxonomically difficult, but ecologically important benthic component. Verhandlungen der Deutschen Zoologischen Gesellschaft **85**.2:271-276
Barthel, D. (1992 b) Do hexactinellids structure Antarctic sponge associations ? Ophelia **36(2)**: 111-118
Barthel, D., Gutt, J. (1992) Sponge associations in the eastern Weddell Sea. Antarctic Science **4(2)**: 137-150
Barthel, D., Gutt, J., Tendal, O. (1991) New information on the biology of Antarctic deep-water sponges derived from underwater photography. Marine Ecology Progress Series **69**: 303-307
Barthel, D., Tendal, O., Panzer K. (1990): Ecology and taxonomy of sponges in the eastern Weddell Sea shelf and slope communities. In: Arntz, W., Ernst, W., Hempel, I. (eds.) The expedition Antarktis VII/4 (Epos leg 3) and VII/5 of RV "Polarstern" in 1989. Berichte zur Polarforschung **68**: 120-130
Belyaev, G. M., Ushakov, P. V. (1957) Some regularities in the quantitative distribution of the benthic fauna in Antarctic waters. The American Institute of Biological Sciences **112**, 116-119. (From Doklady Akademy NAUK SSSR 112, 137-140, Translation [1957])
Bergquist, P. R. (1978) Sponges. Hutchinson & Co. Ltd. London, 268 p
Bidder, G. P. (1923) The relation of the form of a sponge to its currents. Quarterly Journal of microscopic Science **67**: 293-323
--- (1930) On the attitude of a Hexactinellid at the bottom of the sea, as compared with that assumed in museum jars and monographs. The Linnean Society of London, general meeting May 1, protocol p 4-6
Burton, M. (1929) Porifera. Part II. - Antarctic Sponges. British Antarctic ("Terra Nova") Expedition 1910, Zoology **6 (4)**: 393-458
--- (1932) Sponges. Discovery Reports Vol. **6**: 239-392, Cambridge
--- (1934) Sponges. Further zoological results of the Swedish Antarctic Expedition 1901-1903, **3 (2)**, 58 pp, 8 plates
Carter, H. J. (1872) On two new Sponges from the Antarctic Sea, and on a new species of *Tethya* from Shetland; together with observations on the

reproduction of sponges commencing from zygosis of the sponge-animal. The Annals and Magazine of Natural History **9**: 409-435

--- (1875) On the genus *Rossella* (a hexactinellid sponge), with the descriptions of three species. The Annals and Magazine of Natural History Ser. **4 (15)**: 113-122, 1 plate

Coleman, C. O. (1989) On the nutrition of two Antarctic Acanthonotozomatidae (Crustacea: Amphipoda). Polar Biology **9**: 287-294

Dayton, P. K. (1978) Observations of growth, dispersal and population dynamics of some sponges in McMurdo Sound, Antarctica. In: Levi, C., Boury-Esnault, N. (eds.) Biologie des Spongiaires, Coll. Int. Centre Nat. Rech. Sci. **291**: 271-282

Dayton, P. K., Robilliard, G. A., Paine, R. T. (1970) Benthic faunal zonation as a result of anchor ice at McMurdo Sound, Antarctica. In: Holdgate, M. (ed.) Antarctic Ecology, Academic Press, London, **1**: 244-258

Dayton, P. K., Robilliard, G. A., Paine, R. T., Dayton, L. B. (1974) Biological accomodation in the benthic community at McMurdo Sound, Antarctica. Ecological Monographs **44(1)**: 105-128

Dearborn, J. H. (1977) Foods and feeding characteristics of Antarctic asteroids and ophiuroids. In: Llano, G.A (ed.) Adaptations within Antarctic ecosystems. Proc. of the 3rd SCAR Symposium on Antarctic Biology. Smithsonian Institute, Washington, D.C., p. 293-326

Delage, Y., Herouard, E. (1899): Mesozoaires - Spongiaires. Traité de zoologie concrete **2 (1)**, 244 p; Librairie C. Reinwald, Paris

Dell (1972) Antarctic Benthos. Advances in Marine Biology **10**, 1-216.

Feige, W. (1966) Über breitflügelige Anhänge an der Choanocytengeißel von Spongilliden. Die Naturwissenschaften **23**: 617-618

Gutt, J. (1988) Zur Verbreitung und Ökologie der Seegurken (Holothuroidea, Echinodermata) im Weddellmeer (Antarktis). Berichte zur Polarforschung **41**, 86 pp

Hartman, W. D. (1982) Porifera. In: Parker, S. P. (ed.): Synopsis and classification of living organisms, **1**: 640-666; McGraw-Hill Book Company New York, 1166 p.

Ijima, I. (1901) Studies on the Hexactinellida. I.Euplectellidae. Journal of the College of Science of the Imperial University Tokyo **15**: 1-299

--- (1903) Studies on the Hexactinellida. IV. Rossellidae. Journal of the College of Science of the Imperial University Tokyo **18**: 7-307

--- [1] (1927) The hexactinellida of the Siboga Expedition. Siboga-Expeditie VI, 383 p, 26 plates

Kirkpatrick, R. (1907) Porifera. I. - Hexactinellida. National Antarctic Expedition, Natural History **3**, 25 p, 7 plates

125

--- (1910a) On hexactinellid sponge spicules and their names. Annals and Magazine of Natural History, **(8)** 5: 208-213, 1 plate.

--- (1910b) On hexactinellid spicules and their names. Part II. Supplementary. Annals and Magazine of Natural History, **(8)** 5: 347-350.

Koltun, V. M. (1969) Porifera. In: Distribution of selected groups of marine invertebrates in waters south of 35°S latitude. Folio 11, Antarctic Map Folio Series, American Geographical Society.

--- (1976) Porifera - Part I: Antarctic Sponges. B.A.N.Z. Antarctic Research Expedition 1929-1931. Reports - Series B (Zoology and Botany), **9 (4):** 153-198

Kunzmann, K.: Die mit ausgewählten Schwämmen (Hexactinellida und Demospongiae) aus dem Weddellmeer, Antarktis vergesellschaftete Fauna. Berichte zur Polarforschung, in press

Lawn, I. D., Mackie, G. O., Silver G. (1981) Conduction System in a Sponge. Science **211:** 1169-1171

Lendenfeld, R. von (1915) The Sponges. III. Hexactinellida. Memoirs of the Museum of Comparative Zoology **42,** 397 p, 109 plates, Cambridge, USA.

Lévi, C. (1964) Spongiaires des zones bathyale, abyssale et hadale. Galathea Report **7:** 63-112

Mackie, G. O. (1979) Is there a conduction system in sponges? In: Levi, C., Boury-Esnault, N. (eds.) Biology des Spongiaires, Coll. Int. Centre Nat. Rech. Sci. 291: 145-151

Mackie, G. O., Lawn, I. D., Pavans de Ceccatty, M. (1983) Studies on hexactinellid sponges. II. Excitability, conduction and coordination of responses in *Rhabdocalyptus dawsoni* (Lambe, 1873). Philosophical Transactions of the Royal Society of London B. Biol. Sciences **301:** 401-418

Mackie G. O., Singla C. L. (1983) Studies on hexactinellid sponges. I. Histology of *Rhabdocalyptus dawsoni* (Lambe, 1873). Philosophical Transactions of the Royal Society of London B. Biol. Sciences **301:** 365-400

Mehl, D., Reiswig, H. M. (1991) The presence of flagellar vanes in choanomeres of Porifera and their possible phylogenetic implications. Zeitschr. zool. Syst. Evolutionsf. **29(4):** 312-319

Okada, Y. (1928) On the development of a hexactinellid sponge, *Farrea sollasi.* - J. Fac. Sci. Imp. Univ. Tokyo, Sect. 4, **2:** 1-27; Tokyo

Pavans de Ceccatty, M. (1982) *In vitro* aggregation of syncytia and cells of a hexactinellid sponge. Developmental and Comparative Immunology **6:** 15-22

Reid, R. E. H. (1968) Bathymetric distributions of Calcarea and Hexactinellida in the present and the past. Geological Magazine **105:** 546-559

Reiswig, H. M. (1971) The axial symmetry of sponge spicules and its phylogenetic significance. Cahiers de Biologie Marine 12: 505-514

--- (1979) Histology of Hexactinellida (Porifera). In: Levi, C., Boury-Esnault, N. (eds.) Biologie des Spongiaires, Coll. Int. Centre Nat. Rech. Sci. 291: 173-180.

--- (1990) Correction of Ijima's (1927) list of recent hexactinellid sponges (Porifera). Proceedings of the Biological Society of Washington 103(3): 731-745

--- (1991a) New perspectives on the hexactinellid genus Dactylocalyx Stutchbury. In: Reitner J. & H. Keupp (eds.) Fossil and recent sponges, 7-20. Springer-Verlag Berlin Heidelberg, 595 p.

--- (1991b) In situ feeding in two shallow-water hexactinellid sponges, 504-510. In: Rützler, K. (ed.): New perspectives in sponge biology. Proceedings of the Third Intern. Conf. on the Biology of Sponges, Woods Hole, Massachusetts, 1985. Smithsonian Institution Press, Washington, D.C., London, 533 p.

Reiswig, H. M., Mehl D. (1991) Tissue organization of Farrea occa (Porifera, Hexactinellida). Zoomorphology 110 (6): 301-311

Salomon, D., Barthel, D. (1990) External choanosome morphology of the hexactinellid sponge Aulorossella vanhoeffeni Schulze & Kirkpatrick 1910. Senckenbergiana maritima 21: 87-99

Schulze, F. E. (1880) On the structure and arrangement of the soft parts in Euplectella aspergillum. Transactions of the Royal Society of Edinburgh 29: 661-673

--- (1886) Über den Bau und das System der Hexactinelliden. Abhandlungen der Akademie der Wissenschaften zu Berlin, 97 p, Verlag der königlichen Akademie der Wissenschaften Berlin

--- (1887) Report on the Hexactinellida collected by H.M.S. Challenger during the years 1873-1876. Reports on the Scientific Results of the Challenger Expedition. Zoology 21 (53), 514 p, 104 plates, London, Edinburgh, Dublin.

--- (1895) Hexactinelliden des Indischen Oceanes. II. Theil. Die Hexasterophora. Abhandlungen der Königlich Preussischen Akademie der Wissenschaften, 92 p, 8 plates, Verlag der Königlichen Akademie der Wissenschaften Berlin

--- (1897) Revision des Systemes der Asconematiden und Rosselliden. Sitzungsberichte der Königlich Preussischen Akademie der Wissenschaften 26: 520-558

--- (1899) Amerikanische Hexactinelliden nach dem Materiale der Albatross-Expedition, 126 p, 19 plates; Verlag Gustav Fischer, Jena

--- (1904) Hexactinellida. Wissenschaftliche Ergebnisse der Deutschen Tiefsee-Expedition auf dem Dampfer "Valdivia" 1898-1899, **4**, 266 p, 52 plates, Verlag Gustav Fischer Jena.

Schulze, F. E., von Lendenfeld, R. (1889) Über die Bezeichnung der Spongiennadeln. Abhandlungen der Königlich Preussischen Akademie der Wissenschaften Berlin, 1-35

Schulze, F. E., Kirkpatrick, R. (1910a) Preliminary notice on Hexactinellida of the Gauss-Expedition. Zoologischer Anzeiger **35 (9/10)**: 293-302

--- (1910b) Die Hexactinelliden. Deutsche Südpolar-Expedition 1901-1903, 12. Band, Zoologie **4 (1)**: 1-62.

Simpson, T. L. (1984) The cell biology of sponges. Springer Verlag Berlin, Heidelberg, New York, Tokyo, 662 p

Topsent, E. (1901) Notice préliminaire sur les Eponges recueillies par l'éxpedition Antarctique Belge. Archives de Zoologie éxperimentelle et genérale **9 (3)**: 5-16

--- (1902) Spongiaires. Resultats du Voyage du S.Y. Belgica en 1897-1898-1899; 54 p.

--- (1908): Spongiaires. Expedition Antarctique Française (1903-1905). Sciences Naturelles: Documentaire Scientifique, 37 p, 5 plates

--- (1910) Les Hexasterophora recueillies par la Scotia dans l'Antarctique (note preliminaire). Bulletin de l'Institut Oceanographique **166**: 1-18

--- (1912) Sur la contribution apportée par les explorations scientifiques dans l'Antarctique a la connaissance des "Euplectellinae". C.R. Association Française pour l'Avancement des Sciences Sess. **40**: 518-520

--- (1913)[2] Spongiaires de l'expédition Antarctique nationale Ecossaise. Transactions of the Royal Society of Edinburgh **49**: 579-634.

--- (1915a): Une *Rossella* des Açores (*Rossella nodastrella* n. sp.). Bulletin de l'Institut Océanographique de Monaco **303**, 6 p.

--- (1915b) Spongiaires recueillies par la "Scotia" dans l'Antarctique (1903-1904). Transactions of the Royal Society of Edinburgh **51 (1)**: 35-43

--- (1916) Diagnoses d'Eponges recuellies dans l'Antarctique par le "Pour-quoi-pas?". Bulletin du Musée de la Histoire Naturelle **3**:163-172

--- (1917) Spongiaires. Deuxieme Expedition Antarctique Française (1908-1910), commandé par Dr. Jean Charcot. Sciences Physiques Documents Scientifiques, 88 p, 6 plates.

Tuzet, O. (1973) Hexactinellides ou Hyalosponges (Triaxonia F. E. Schulze). p 633-690 in: Grassé P.-P. (ed.) Spongiaires. Traité de Zoologie **3 (1)**, Paris

Ushakov, P. V. (1964) Benthic operations of the Soviet Antarctic Expedition on the "OB" (1956-1958). Soviet Antarctic Expedition Information Bulletin, Vol. I, Elsevier Amsterdam London New York, 116-119.

Voss, J. (1988) Zoogeographie und Gemeinschaftsanalyse des Makrozoobenthos des Weddellmeeres (Antarktis). Berichte zur Polarforschung **45**, 145 pp.

Wägele, J.-W. (1988) Aspects of the Life-Cycle of the Antarctic Fish Parasite *Gnathia calva* Vanhöffen (Crustacea: Isopoda). Polar Biology **8**: 287-291

---

[1] The date on the volume is 1926, but it became available only during the year 1927, and should therefore be cited under this year. Compare Reiswig (1990).

[2] Published again in the year 1920 in: Report on the scientific results of the voyage of S.Y. "Scotia" during the years 1902, 1903 and 1904, Vol. 7 - Zoology, p 3-72, 6 plates.

129

11. INDEX

APPENDIX: PLATES

Plate I: *Chonelasma lamella*. Fragment, where both the smooth outer (incurrent) side and porous inner (excurrent) side are visible. EPOS St. 253, Halley Bay, 2012 m depth. Height 10 cm.

Plate II: *Chonelasma lamella*. Fragments showing the hollow, partly tubular growthform of the species. EPOS St. 253, Halley Bay, 2012 m depth. Height 4 cm (both specimens).

Plate III: *Rossella racovitzae*. Small specimen which was attached to small stones and gravel by means of stiltlike extensions. In this specimen, the conules typical for the species are not well developped. EPOS St. 249, Halley Bay, 699 m depth. Height 13 cm.

138

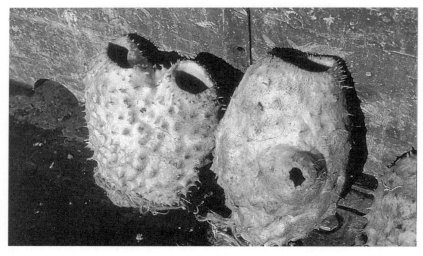

Plate IV: *Rossella racovitzae*. Two specimens with double- and side osculum respectively. Height ca. 35-40 cm. Note the small conules with remainders of protruding spicule tufts. EPOS, Halley Bay.

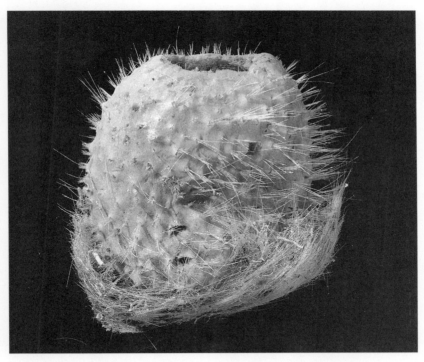

Plate V: *Rossella villosa*. Complete specimen. Note the numerous small conules with remainders of well developped spicule tufts and massive basal spicule tuft. Specimen about 20 cm high. EPOS St. 230, Halley Bay, 275 m depth.

Plate VI: *Rossella fibulata.* Largest specimen, height about 60 cm, weight about 12 kg. Note the very large, rounded conules which lack spicule tufts. EPOS St. 230, Halley Bay, 275 m depth.

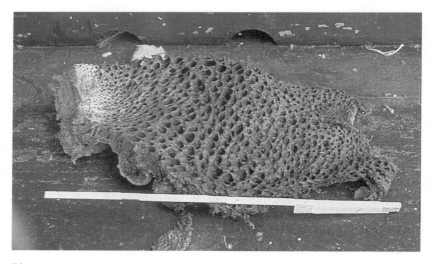

Plate VII: *Rossella fibulata.* Inner (excurrent) side of the specimen shown in Plate VI; sponge basis to the right. Note the large openings of the excurrent canals that are not covered by a sievelike spicule mesh.

Plate VIII: *Rossella fibulata.* Young specimen. Note the round, tuftless conules in the lower part, the upper part which does not bear conules, and the weakly developped basal spicule tuft. EPOS St. 230, Halley Bay, 275 m depth. Height 40 cm.

Plate IX: *Rossella nuda.* Double specimen. It is unclear, whether two individuals merged or one individual split to produce this structure. Note the completely smooth surface and the weakly developed basal spicule tuft. EPOS St. 230, Halley Bay, 275 m depth. Height of larger specimen 19 cm.

143

Plate X: *Rossella nuda.* Inner side. The openings of the excurrent canals are usually covered with a lacelike dermal spicule mesh, but this can be torn off during catch. EPOS St. 230, Halley Bay, 275 m depth. Height 42 cm.

Plate XI: *Rossella levis*. Complete specimen. Characteristic are the numerous small conules. The spicule tufts emerging from the lower and basal conules serve to anchor the sponge in the substrate. EPOS St. 224, Kapp Norvegia, 186 m depth. Height 14 cm.

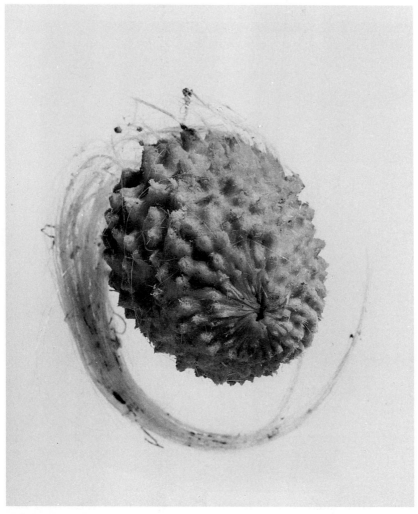

Plate XII: *Rossella levis*. Same specimen as in Plate XI. Note the extremely contracted osculum. Diameter 7 cm.

Plate XIII: *Rossella vanhoeffeni*. Close-up of outer (incurrent) side. Note the smooth, fine-meshed texture. EPOS St. 261, Halley Bay, 799 m depth. Height 10 cm.

Plate XIV: *Rossella vanhoeffeni.* Close-up of inner (excurrent) side of the same specimen shown in Plate XIII. The openings of the excurrent canals are covered with a lacelike dermal spicule mesh.

Plate XV: *Rossella vanhoeffeni*. Two specimens with entwined, very massive spicule tufts. Note the completely smooth surface and the strongly contracted osculum in the larger specimen. The contracted hole at the side probably arises from a former injury, maybe the grazing mark of a predator. EPOS St. 224, Kapp Norvegia, 186 m depth. Height of larger specimen 12 cm.

Plate XVI: *Bathydorus spinosus*. Complete specimen. Note the funnel shape, small spicule bearing conules in the lower part and attachment to a small stone. EPOS St. 253, Halley Bay, 2012 m depth. Height 19 cm.

Plate XVII: *Bathydorus spinosus*. Complete specimen. Note the very thin oscular margin, very small incurrent dermal openings on the outer side and larger excurrent openings on the inner surface. EPOS St. 253, Halley Bay, 2012 m depth. Height 13 cm.

Plate XVIII: *Bathydorus spinosus*. Two small specimens, one with a double osculum. In the small specimens, the typical shape is already attained, but the spicule tuft bearing conules are not yet developed. EPOS St. 253, Halley Bay, 2012 m depth. Height of larger specimen 6 cm.

Plate XIX: *Scolymastra joubini.* Complete specimen. Note the smooth surface and short, but massive basal spicule tuft. The scar in the middle of the specimen stems from grazing activity of a dorid nudibranch. EPOS St. 224, Kapp Norvegia, 186 m depth. Height 21 cm.

Plate XX: *Scolymastra joubini.* Inner side of the specimen shown in Plate XIX. Characteristic are the thick, massive walls. The excurrent openings are covered by a lacelike spicule mesh with larger pores in the basal part of the sponge. Height 21 cm.

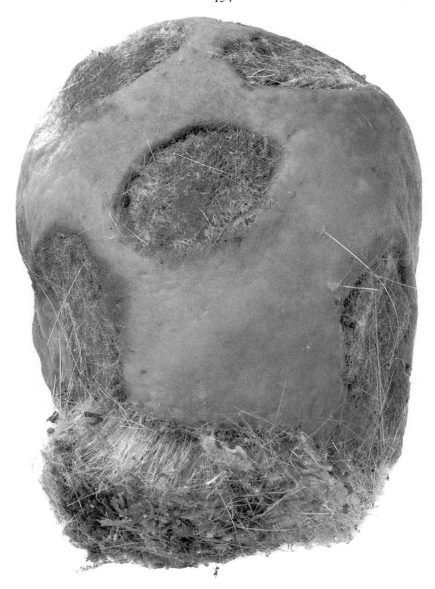

Plate XXI: *Scolymastra joubini*. Complete specimen covered with large scars from the feeding activity of dorid nudibranchs. EPOS St. 224, Kapp Norvegia, 186 m depth. Height 10 cm.